KU-198-038

Museum of **São Roque**

GUIDE

CREDITS

General coordination
Maria Helena Oliveira

Scientific coordination
Teresa Freitas Morna

Texts
History of the museum and introduction to the sections – Helena Alexandra Soares Mantas
Altar frontals – Maria Filomena Brito
Chapel of Saint John the Baptist – António Filipe Pimentel
Flemish tapestry – Helena Alexandra Soares Mantas
Chapel of Saint John the Baptist – Teresa Leonor Vale
Metalworks – António Meira Marques Henriques and Helena Alexandra Soares Mantas
Model of the Chapel of Saint John the Baptist – António Meira Marques Henriques
Oriental art – Maria do Carmo Lino and Teresa Freitas Morna
Painting – António Meira Marques Henriques, Helena Alexandra Soares Mantas,
Maria Filomena Brito and Teresa Freitas Morna
Reliquaries – António Meira Marques Henriques
Sculpture – Maria Filomena Brito and Teresa Freitas Morna
Textiles of the Chapel of Saint John the Baptist – Magda Tassinari

Revision
Maria João Ferreira (textiles)
Maria Madalena Requixa

Translation
Thomas Fisher

Secretariat
Elisabete Moreno
Fátima Rodrigues

Design
Luis Chimeno Garrido

3D images
Ricardo Viegas

Photographic Credits
António Homem Cardoso; Archivo dell'Arte, Nápoles – Luciano Pedicini; Cintra & Castro Caldas, Lda.;
Direcção de Comunicação e Imagem da Santa Casa da Misericórdia de Lisboa / Núcleo de Audiovisuais
e Multimédia – Carlos Sousa; Henrique Ruas; Instituto dos Museus e da Conservação, Divisão de
Documentação Fotográfica – Luísa Oliveira; Júlio Marques; Manuel Lemos; Pedro Aboim Borges;
Soprintendenza per il P.S.A.E. e del Polo Museale della Città di Napoli, Naples

Support
Co-financied by FEDER – Programa Operacional da Cultura

Photographic treatment of images and printing
Facsimile, Lda.

Lisbon, November 2008
100 copies

ISBN: 978-972-8761-33-2
Legal deposit: 285349/08

THE BRITISH MUSEUM
THE PAUL HAMLYN LIBRARY

069 · 09469 MuS

contents

The Santa Casa da Misericórdia de Lisboa has for its 510 years of existence been bringing together a heritage of great social, historic and artistic value, from donations, inheritance and acquisitions.

Part of the patrimonial collection is found kept at the Museum of São Roque, created in 1905, with the intention of exhibiting the important Treasure of the Chapel of Saint John the Baptist, an unsurpassed reference in the study of 18th century European art.

Since its creation, the museum has been accompanying the operational changes in the domain of museology, seeking to meet the ever more rigorous demands which were imposed in the fields of patrimonial preservation, study and promotion.

The most recent remodelling of the Museum of São Roque stemmed from the will of Santa Casa da Misericórdia de Lisboa to correct a series of limitations in many senses, namely to improve the accessibility and increase the permanent exhibition area, thus creating reception and support structures which are considered essential in a cultural space which wants to meet the standards of contemporary reality.

It is important to highlight that this project is not an isolated action, but is part of a wider context, of creation of a dynamic cultural pole, which involves, apart from the Museum of São Roque, the Church of São Roque and the Historical Archive of Misericórdia de Lisboa. In fact, considering that the Museum of São Roque and the Church of São Roque constitute an inseparable whole, the Misericórdia de Lisboa is also developing a programme of improvement of the latter, featuring the recent renovation of its lighting system, the renovation of the Altar pieces in gilded wood of the Chapels of Our Lady of Doctrine and of the Holy Sacrament and the renovation project of its main façade. On the other hand, since 2007 the Historical Archive is also to be found working in the headquarters of the Misericórdia de Lisboa, in Largo Trindade Coelho, in new installations, duly equipped and prepared to receive the public and to better guarantee the preservation of its contents.

With the remodelling/enlarging project of the Museum of São Roque finished, which counted on the helpful financial support of the *Programa Operacional da Cultura*, the museum has reopened to the public as a modernised space, which dignifies the exhibited patrimony and offers conditions of comfort and well-being to its visitors.

In this way, Santa Casa da Misericórdia de Lisboa hopes to increase the curiosity and interest of the public for a group of collections of extreme representativeness of Portuguese, European and Luso-Oriental Art. Simultaneously, the valuation of the Church and of the Museum of São Roque, situated next to Chiado and Bairro Alto areas where thousands of both national and foreign tourists pass, will constitute a contribution to the promotion of historical and artistic patrimony of the city of Lisbon and of Portugal.

Rui António Ferreira da Cunha
The *Provedor* of Santa Casa da Misericórdia de Lisboa

The Museum of São Roque is installed in the space of the old Professed House of the Society of Jesus in Lisbon, a building connected to the Church of São Roque. It opened to the public in 1905 with the name *Museu do Thesouro da Capela de São João Baptista* (Museum of the Treasure of the Chapel of Saint John the Baptist), evoking the important collection of Italian Art from which its creation originates. In the thirties the context of the museum was broadened, exhibiting a wider variety of pieces and emerging with the name *Museu de Arte Sacra de São Roque* (The Museum of Religious Art of São Roque). In the sixties it gained new meaning in being explicitly associated with the Church of São Roque, and thus being introduced into the concept of Monument Museum. In the nineties the reinforcing of the link was sought through the creation of new exhibition sections. More recently the museum has seen its area grow considerably which has allowed the collection on exhibition to diversify and create new support structures. With the intention of reinforcing the museum and church connection, a renovation of the architectonic elements of the old Professed House of São Roque has proceeded, such as the cloister and old areas of access between the two spaces.

The collection of the Museu de São Roque, essentially constituting pieces of metalwork, vestments, sculpture, painting and reliquaries, together with the exceptional contents of the collection of the Chapel of Saint John the Baptist, makes up an unequalled representation of History of Art in Portugal and in Europe over five centuries. Within the group of exhibited works, the section of Oriental Art is a fulcrum, being widely representative of the Portuguese in the Orient, in particular in the way the Society of Jesus was distinguished abroad, both on the evangelical and cultural level.

With the aim of facilitating a better understanding to the visiting public of the artistic collection of Santa Casa da Misericórdia de Lisboa, the Museum of São Roque has sought to develop a systematic policy of publications, with a view to broaden the offer of the contents to a wider audience.

It is in this context, in complement to the permanent catalogue and other promotional material, that this guide is published, in both Portuguese and English, in order to make the contents of the museum more accessible to all its visitors and, consequently, facilitate deciphering the museological collection.

With the goal of helping the visitor and better serving the community, this guide of the permanent exhibition, which covers the most representative pieces of the collection, is structured according to the museological route, following the order of the presentation of the different thematic sections of the museum.

One hopes that this written support meets the different interests of the public, including foreign visitors, who have an expressive representation in the context of cultural tourism, who seek the museum and Church of São Roque.

Teresa Freitas Morna
Curator of the Museum of São Roque

Main façade of the museum in 1905

to be valued in our country. Although the foundation of the museological space in the strictest sense of the term, was dated 1905, at the end of the 19th century the preoccupation of the Misericórdia de Lisboa to promote its important artistic collection to the public was already evident.

In 1898, on the *4th centenary of the Foundation of Santa Casa da Misericórdia de Lisboa* celebrations, the liturgical utensils and vestments from the

First presentation
of the Treasure
of the Chapel
of Saint John the Baptist,
in the sacristy
of the Church
of São Roque, 1898

Treasure of the Chapel of Saint John the Baptist in the Church of São Roque were shown to the public for the first time, in the sacristy of the church, having been adapted for the occasion. The commemorations of the year of Vasco de Gama's arrival in India significantly contributed to the success of this initiative, as Chiado was one of the main centres of the celebrations which took place.

The awakened curiosity and the interest for this display prompted the permanent presentation of the Treasure of the Chapel of Saint John the Baptist in a larger space, thus bringing about the *Museu do Thesouro da Capela de São João Baptista* (Museum of the Treasure of the Chapel of Saint John the Baptist). The next step consisted of choosing a location to host the museum and the architect responsible for the elaboration of the project. For the location, the old Lottery Room was chosen, which was in one of the parts of the old Professed House of São Roque, the annex building to the Church. To draw up the project of the new museum, Misericórdia invited Arnaldo Adães Bermudes, the architect responsible for other architectonic projects commissioned by the Institution at the time, such as the neo-manueline tomb of the benefactors, in the cemetery of Alto de São João.

Interior of the museum after its foundation, in 1905

Interior view of the museum after remodelling
by Jorge Cid, in 1931

After the work was completed, the museum was solemnly inaugurated on
11th January, 1905, in the presence of King Carlos I and Queen Amélia.
Following the museographic criteria of the time, the objective was to have
a large presentation of the objects, accommodating the new room with
various showcases.

Accompanying changes in museology, the museum underwent a series
of interventions throughout the 20th century, three of which stand out.
The first important renovation occurred between 1929 and 1931, under the
mandate of *Provedor* José da Silva Ramos, in a wider context of a policy
of modernisation initiated by Misericórdia de Lisboa. The museum, then
run by Jorge Cid, was enlarged, going on to occupy two new rooms, which
allowed the unknown collections to be presented, such as the painting
collection and Portuguese metalwork collection. Showcases with discrete
lines were installed in these rooms, the preoccupation of highlighting the
aesthetic values of the objects being well known.

The hitherto *Museu do Thesouro da Capela de São João Baptista* emerged
now as the *Museu de Arte Sacra de S. Roque* (The Museum of Religious Art
of São Roque).

Interior view of one room of the museum, after remodelling
by Maria João Madeira Rodrigues, in 1968

In the sixties the museum was the object of another important
museographic intervention, under the responsibility of Curator Maria João
Madeira Rodrigues and of Architect Fernando Peres Guimarães, who
counted on the support of the Calouste Gulbenkian Foundation. The completion
of this project – today considered one of the museographical marks in
Portugal of the 60's – dramatically altered the discourse of the museum.
In order to reduce the previous exhibition load, they chose to circumscribe
the exhibition to essential works of art. The collection of the Chapel
of Saint John the Baptist came to occupy practically the whole area of
the museum, a new section having been created which was destined for
the exhibition of the collections of Portuguese origins, in an annex to
the sacristy of the church, renovated for that reason. With the objective
of clarifying the understanding of the pieces, new aluminium display cases
were installed, a material which was starting to be used. Maria João
Madeira Rodrigues proposed the classification of the museum as a
Monument Museum, for the specificity of being linked to the Church of São
Roque and to the Chapel of Saint John the Baptist, refuting the
classification as Museum of Sacred Art.
Still in the 20th century an intervention in 1993 stood out, a result of the
joint work of curator Nuno Vassallo e Silva and of Architect João Bento

Interior view of one room of the museum, after remodelling
by Nuno Vassallo e Silva, in 1993

e Almeida. The museological discourse was mainly altered restricting the
Treasure of the Chapel of Saint John the Baptist to one of the larger rooms
of the museum, and the works which had not been presented to the public
were installed in the remaining rooms. This project sought to reinforce the
link between the museum and the church, presenting four sections:
the *Manueline Shrine of São Roque*, *Society of Jesus*, *Chapel of Saint John the
Baptist* and the *Misericórdia de Lisboa*. On this occasion, the annex gallery
to the sacristy of the church was newly renovated for the presentation
of temporary exhibitions.

Despite the mentioned renovations which stand out for the size of the
alterations which were introduced in the museological discourse, others,
of smaller scale, assume a significant role in the history of the museum,
namely the interventions carried out by Pedro da Cunha Santos, Curator
of the museum in the 40's and by Matilde Sousa Franco, in the 90's.

The new museological project

The most recent remodelling of the Museum of São Roque stemmed from
the will of Santa Casa da Misericórdia de Lisboa to revamp its patrimony

General view of the Church of São Roque

and correct a series of long felt limitations, namely the exiguity of the space of the museum which forced a considerable part of its collection to be kept in reserves and made the creation of reception and support areas impossible.

Taking the space of the museum and the church as a whole, its was sought to reinforce the unity between these two spaces which has had repercussions in both the architectonic project, namely in the option for the reopening of accesses between the two spaces which had been blocked and in the museological space, where he sought to establish a clear connection between the exhibited pieces and their place of origin in the church, in particular with respect to the altar piece, pictorial sets and the collection of reliquaries. The inclusion of multimedia points on the route of the exhibition reinforces this strong link between the church and the museum.

The space of the museum is organised in harmony with the old sixteen hundreds Jesuit cloister, renovated in the context of this project and object

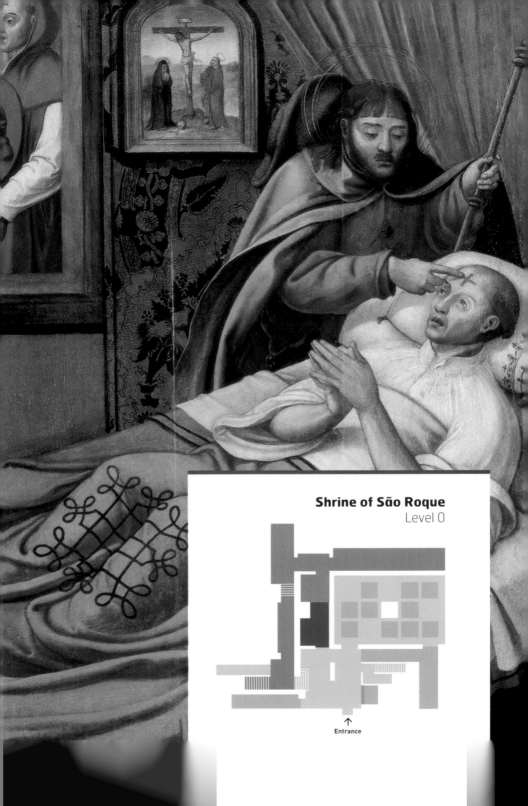

Shrine of São Roque
Level 0

↑
Entrance

The trilogy of hunger, pestilence and war made up the strongest fear of the medieval imagination. Pestilence, the name given to all the diseases of epidemic nature – the black death, cholera, typhoid and smallpox among others – caused thousands of deaths all over Europe. Amongst these diseases was the black death, which emerged in Europe in 1347. According to some authors, this epidemic would have come from Crimea, others believe it originated in the Far East, probably China. In fact, the consequences of the plague were determinant in the development of European History, resulting in serious crises on a social and economic level, which were felt all over Europe in the second half of the 14th century due to the high morbidity caused by this disease. The black death arrived in Portugal in 1348, affecting above all the cities where the contagion was particularly rife due to poor health and hygiene conditions. Henceforth and until the 16th century, the Portuguese territory was intermittently ravaged by various waves of pestilence.

In 1505, Lisbon was hit by a severe wave of pestilence brought by a Venetian ship. The King Manuel I (1495-1521) therefore asked the Republic of Venice for a relic of Saint Roch, a saint who was born in the 14th century, in Montpellier (France), whose miracles to help those afflicted with the plague were very popular in meridional Europe. The relic of the saint, which would have arrived in Lisbon in 1505, was solemnly received by the Court and by the people of the city and taken in procession to a field outside the city walls, next to the Tower of Álvaro Pais. A small shrine dedicated to Saint Roch would be built on this very spot to host the relic, which was consecrated by Bishop D. Duarte, on the 25th February, 1515, a fact proven by the text of a plaque currently kept at the museum. Another plaque tells us that the churchyard of the shrine, in which victims

Stone inscription of the churchyard of the shrine
Portugal, 1527
Limestone
51,5 x 79,3 x 0,5 cm
Inv. Esc. 181

Saint Roch
Portugal, 16th century (early)
Polychrome limestone
154 x 80 x 50 cm
Inv. Esc. 202

of the plague were buried, was consecrated by Bishop D. Ambrosio, in 1527. When the building of the shrine was finished, a brotherhood was established invoking Saint Roch, which remains to this day.

With the arrival of the first priests of the Society of Jesus in Lisbon, in 1540, the site of the shrine was the place chosen for the building of their Church and Professed House.

Construction started in the reign of King João III (1521-1557), being completed during the dominion of King Filipe II of Spain, I of Portugal (1581-1598). Despite the demolition of the shrine, the devotion of Saint Roch continued in the current church through the respective Brotherhood. An agreement established between them and the priests of the Society of Jesus stated that the church would receive the invocation of Saint Roch and which would be worshipped inside in a chapel dedicated to the protector of the plagued. The actual Chapel of São Roque was constructed in the place of the high altar of the old shrine, this was proven in archeological work carried out in 1998, while reinforcing the foundations of the church. The work shed light on some traces of the shrine, although they were

Chapel of Saint Roch, Church of São Roque, retable of the 18th century (early)

scarce and fragmented, essentially skeletal, traces of the architectonic structures and painted tiles[1].

The first exhibition section of the museum is dedicated to the memory of the Shrine of São Roque, displaying works directly linked with this and the devotion to the saint. Featured amongst the exhibited works in this section is the set of four oil painted panels, illustrating the life legend of Saint Roch, which belonged to the old altar piece of the shrine. Attributed to Jorge Leal and more recently to Cristovão de Utreque and painted around 1520, each one of the four paintings shows two stages of the saint's life simultaneously[2].

In the exhibition sector the reconstitution of the original arrangement of the four panels on the altar piece of the shrine has been sought, which would certainly follow a narrative programme – a simple narrative, which is linear and easily understood by the faithful, following the chronology of the life of Saint Roch. A tabernacle and a sculpture of Saint Roch would have occupied the centre of the altar piece, flanked by two panels on either side, arranged vertically. The sequence would have been from left to right and from bottom to top. Thus at the bottom would have been the two first panels, *Birth and adolescence of Saint Roch and Miraculous Cure of the Cardinal* and *recognition of the miracle by the Pope* – above would have been the panels *Stay in Piacenza and retreat to the forest* and *Imprisonment and beatific death of Saint Roch*[3].

Also exhibited in this section are the two inscribed plaques which were mentioned previously, pieces which constitute an important testimony of the old shrine: one commemorative of its building and anointment, dated 1515 and another commemorative of consecration of its churchyard, with the date 1527. ∎

1. Maria Ramalho, Miguel Soromenho, Ana Nunes, Catarina Serpa, Ana Santos and Cláudia Umbelino, "Da antiga Ermida à Igreja e Casa Professa de S. Roque: alguns vestígios arqueológicos e antropológicos", in *A Ermida Manuelina de São Roque*, Museu de São Roque, Lisbon, 1999, pp. 17-35.
2. Fernando António Baptista Pereira, *Imagens e Histórias de devoção. Espaço, tempo e narrativa na Pintura Portuguesa do Renascimento*, Doctorate Dissertation presented to the Faculdade de Belas Artes da Universidade de Lisboa, Lisbon, 2000, pp. 394-404.
3. Joaquim Oliveira Caetano, *Pintura. Século XVI ao século XX*, Vol. I, Museu de São Roque, Lisbon, 1998, pp.40-41; Fernando António Baptista Pereira, *Imagens e Histórias de devoção. Espaço, tempo e narrativa na Pintura Portuguesa do Renascimento*, Doctorate Dissertation presented to the Faculdade de Belas Artes da Universidade de Lisboa, Lisbon, 2000, p. 404.

Panels of Saint Roch
Jorge Leal/Cristóvão de Utreque (?)
Portugal, c. 1520
Oil on wood
128 x 119 cm
Inv. Pin. 52, Pin. 53, Pin. 55 and Pin. 56

This set of four panels dedicated to the life and legend of Saint Roch made up part of the great altar-piece of the old Shrine of São Roque, constructed in 1505. Documentation that reveals the identification of this pictorial set is not yet known. Nevertheless, based on stylistic comparisons with similar works, and in the reading of a small inscription which is visible on one of the panels that make up the set, Garcia Fernandes, Jorge Leal and more recently Cristovão de Utreque have all been suggested as being the authors of these works.

These four paintings stand out for their narrative capacity managed through the recourse of duplication of scenes within the space of the painting, in each of the panels two distinct episodes of the life and legend of the saint are represented: in the foreground, the chronologically first episode; in the background, the second episode, inserted in the scenery or seen through a window, in the latter case with the effect of a painting within a painting. As for the position of the panels on the altar-piece, they would have certainly obeyed simple narrative criteria, easily understood by the faithful, with the narrative being read from left to right and from bottom to top, with the scenes being arranged according to the linear chronology of the events, with the top area of the altar-piece reserved for the most edifying episodes of the life of the saint.

I. Birth and adolescence of Saint Roch

The representation of the birth of Saint Roch, displays strong parallelisms with the representations of the birth of the Virgin or of Saint John the Baptist. On the left hand side of the composition we can see the mother of Saint Roch who is recovering from the birth, lying on a bed and a nurse who offers her soup. In the middle a woman prepares the bath of the new-born, whom she holds, showing him to the father and two other masculine figures. The mark of the cross on the chest of the child identifies him as Saint Roch. Of note are the representations of the day to day elements which enrich the composition: a bowl of soup served with an Afro-Portuguese ivory spoon, the box of marmalade over the bed and a sewing basket, and the little stove with a copper frying pan on the floor.

In the background, on the right, with recourse to the scheme of a painting within a painting, the painter represented the moment in which the saint abandoned the mundane life to start a life of pilgrimage: Saint Roch, with a

cape and the hat of a pilgrim, distributing alms to a group of poor who kneel before him, in a gesture of thanks.

II. Miraculous cure of the Cardinal and recognition of the miracle by the Pope

In this panel the episode of Saint Roch's miraculous cure of the English cardinal in Piacenza is represented in the foreground. The saint, standing next to the bed of the ill, traces the sign of the cross on his forehead. At the foot of the cardinal's bed, we can observe the cardinalate clothes, which identify him, and a cup and two jars placed on a wooden bench. Two youths, with their arms raised and kneeling at the foot of the bed of the cardinal, attend the miraculous cure. On the wall, one can see a small painting with the representation of Calvary.

In the background, on the left hand side, and according to the same compositional scheme as the previously described painting, we find a scene of recognition of the miracle by the Pope.

III. Stay in Piacenza and retreat in the forest

In what would be the third panel of the set we can see, in the foreground, Saint Roch leaving a building, visibly afflicted with the plague, – as much by the expression of his face as by the open wound on his leg – being led by a man who invites him to leave the area. Bed ridden patients can be seen through an arch which opens in the wall of the building. This covers the episode of Saint Roch's sojourn in Piacenza to help the plagued.

The wall of the churchyard of the building marks the separation between these two scenes represented in this panel.

The second episode – *Retreat of Saint Roch in the forest* – is represented as background scenery. The saint, lying at the entrance of a straw hut, can be seen being surrounded by a dog which fed him daily with bread during this period of retreat and the angel which applied a miraculous balm on his wounds which would save the benefactor from death.

IV. Imprisonment and beatific death of Saint Roch

The final panel of the set presents a greater dynamism than the other three, which is owed to the quantity of human figures represented and the diversity of their poses. In the foreground features Saint Roch's imprisonment, which happened on his return to Montpellier for not being recognised. The saint was accused of espionage and is led by the soldiers to the presence of the Duke of the city who orders him to be arrested. Various noble figures watch the imprisonment.

In the background on the left, relying on the scheme of a painting within a painting, we can see the death of Saint Roch, which happened in prison. The saint, discovered dead by a group of women, is found shackled and lying down with his hands in a gesture of prayer.

On the right hand side of the composition, there is a landscape in the background.

Society of Jesus
Level 1

Society of Jesus
Level 0

↑
Entrance

The Society of Jesus was founded by Saint Ignatius of Loyola in 1534 and approved by Pope Paul III, in 1540, by way of Papal bull *Regimini Militantis Ecclesiae*.

The Portuguese Crown immediately showed interest in entrusting to the Fathers of the Society of Jesus the evangelisation of the Orient. Thus, João III, then king of Portugal, entrusted D. Pedro de Mascarenhas, Portuguese ambassador in Rome with the mission to promote the coming of the Society of Jesus to Portugal. Simão Rodrigues and Francis Xavier arrived in Portugal as soon as 1540. The former stayed to organise the Portuguese Province of the Society, the latter left for the Orient in 1541. The Period of Jesuit expansion in Continental Portugal, the Orient and Brazil thereby starting, accompanied by a vast programme of aesthetic and artistic renovation, conceived in harmony with the rules imposed by the counter-reformist liturgy.

Initially the Jesuits stayed in the Hospital of Todos-os-Santos in Rossio, they later moved to the old Convent of Santo Antão, of the *Cónegos Regrantes de Santo Agostinho*. The fathers of the Society began to develop their preaching activity next to the small shrine of São Roque, which they immediately considered as the ideal location to construct their church and professed house.

Despite early opposition from the Brotherhood of São Roque in relation to the construction of the home of Jesuits in the location of the shrine, as it would mean its destruction, the Society of Jesus, which enjoyed wide privileges from the Court, managed to fulfil their intention.

In the 18th century, in 1759, during the reign of King José I (1755-1777) and the government of Marquês de Pombal, the Society of Jesus was expelled from Portugal. Soon after, in 1768, the patrimony of São Roque, including its furniture, was donated to Santa Casa da Misericórdia de Lisboa. This donation had extremely important consequences, seeing as it allowed for an integral set of important collections to be kept, including paintings, sculptures, metalwork and vestments, keeping it safe from the expropriations which accompanied the extinction of the religious orders in Portugal by the Liberals in 1834.

The section of the museum dedicated to the Society of Jesus documents the two centuries of the Order in São Roque, opening with a set of portraits of figures who played, either directly or indirectly, an important role in the foundation of this Jesuit house: Saint Ignatius of Loyola, the founder of the Society of Jesus in Portugal; King João III and Queen Catarina of Austria, monarch that promoted the settlement of the Order in Portugal; and Saint Francis Borgia, Third General of the Society, active supporter of the construction of the Church and Professed House of São Roque. The latter holds particular significance in São Roque as his son, D. João de Borgia, gave a set of notable reliquaries to the church in 1587. This section is developed according a thematic logic, being subdivided into *iconography and devotions of the Order and Object of Liturgical use and church decoration.*

Iconography of the Order

The presence and action of the Society of Jesus were particularly reinforced by the creation of their own iconography, in which the symbol of the order – IHS (*Iesus Hominum Salvator* – Jesus Saviour of Men) – and the representation of its founders were featured. In Portugal, and in the case of the Church and the Professed House of São Roque, this iconography emerges associated to the most varied artistic mediums, such as painting, sculpture, textiles, painted tiles, through which the great actions and miracles of Saints of the Society are skilfully illustrated for catechetical purposes.
Saint Ignatius of Loyola (1491-1556), the founder of the Society of Jesus, his companion and Missionary of the Orient, Saint Francis Xavier (1506--1552), Saint Francis Borgia (1510-1572), Third General of the Society, and Stanislas Kostka (1550-1568), a Polish young man who gave up everything to enter the Society, are figures who are represented in the museum through a set of paintings and sculptures from the 17th century.

Monogram of the Society of Jesus
Tempera on stucco, 17th century,
sacristy of Church of São Roque

Main devotions

Being directly associated with the Catholic Counter-Reformation, the Society of Jesus would put into practice the decisions from the Council of Trent, between 1545 and 1563, with the aim of assuring the unity of faith and ecclesiastic discipline at a time of crisis in the heart of the Catholic Church, resulting from the reformist movement started by Martin Luther from which the Protestant Churches were born.

The Council of Trent clarified doctrinal questions related to Salvation, Eucharist and the Sacraments, as well as regular liturgical rituals, namely mass, with a view to its uniformity in all the Catholic world. A list of prohibited books was also instituted – *Index Librorum Prohibitorum* – and it reorganised the Inquisition.

The Society of Jesus, created in this context, promoted the devotion of death, which it adapted to the new catechismal purposes of the Catholic Church, in particular, aiming at creating a policy of captivating the believers, by drawing their attention to the brevity of terrestrial life, thus causing a strong and generalised feeling of fear.

In this process of spreading of the devotion to death and suffering the image was of core importance, shown by the multiplication of works dedicated to this theme, in particular to scenes of the Passion of Christ or the Martyrs. The contemplation of the material traces of saints – bone fragments, hair, clothing material, amongst others, – was understood, in the context of the Counter-Reformation, as a privileged vehicle for the faithful to reach Salvation, thereby a true "industry" of reliquaries developed to house the numerous relics which were then so venerated. These works, of metalwork, sculpture and furniture, generally of great artistic quality, can be divided into five main categories: reliquary busts, reliquary arms, monstrance-

Arm-Reliquary of Saint Amance
Portugal, 17th century
Silver and gilt wood
67,2 x 15 x 16 cm
Inv. Rl. 297

-reliquaries, *a tabula* reliquary, casket or box reliquaries and, finally, the wide group of sculpture reliquaries both showcases and hanging.

The number of pieces exhibited in the Museum and Church of São Roque dedicated to the cycles of the Passion and the Glorification of Christ is significant. In so far as the devotion to the Martyr Saints is concerned, there is an important group of relics and their respective reliquaries which are kept in the Museum and Church of São Roque, most the results of the great donation made to the Society of Jesus, in 1587, by D. João de Borgia, son of Saint Francis Borgia and ambassador of King Felipe II of Spain, in Saxony. The Marian devotion also had special receptivity within the iconography dictated by Trent, which explains the creation of so many brotherhoods linked to the Virgin Mary based in Chapels of the Church of São Roque, as well as the large number of representations of the Virgin Mary, in particular, the themes of the Annunciation, Piety and Assumption. Exhibited on the ground floor are works from the Church and old

Reliquary *A Tabula*
Portugal, 17th century (2nd half)
Ebony, gilt bronze, coloured glass
and tempera painting on paper
101 x 73 x 17
Inv. Rl. 208

Professed House of São Roque, which testify the main devotions of the Fathers who inhabited the space, with particular emphasis on the martyr saints. In the presentation of the reliquary collection, establishing a link with the altars of the relics of the Church of São Roque was intended, recreating their configuration in a manner which is simplified and adapted to the contemporary museological language. So, next to these reliquaries there are four paintings dedicated to the theme of martyrdom which originally covered the altars of the relics of the Church.

Along the staircase and on the upper floor of the museum, one can see pieces related to the theme of the life of Christ and of the Virgin Mary. The life of Christ is presented to us in a reverse chronological narrative sequence. We begin with the end of Christ's life, represented through an 18th century sculpture of Risen Christ followed by his death on the cross, the way to Calvary, the prayer on the Mount of Olives, and the ceremony of the Washing the Feet. From then on the chronological sequence is interrupted and, in a flash back, we are taken to the context of the birth of Christ, beginning with the genealogy of the Virgin Mary, presented through works which represent her parents, Saints Joachin and Anne. Followed we can see the representations of the Virgin Mary with the Infant Jesus and Nativity scenes such as the Adoration of the Shepherds and of the Magi.

Objects of liturgical use and church ornamentation: staging of religious ceremonies

The ornamentation of the churches and staging of religious ceremonies were an important instrument in the propagation of new schemes dictated by the post-Tridentine Catholicism. If the chapels of the Church of São Roque are exuberant in their decoration today, they were even more so in the past due to the adornments placed on the altars, pulpits and altar pieces, namely door hangings, pelmets, tabernacle pavilions, decorative covers and missal stand covers.

Amongst the decorations of the temple of São Roque which reached us, there features a set of altar frontals from the 17th century, now exhibited in the museum. These richly embroidered textiles, which in the past were placed on the vertical part of the altars held an important role in the

Altar frontal
Portugal, 17th century
Ground fabric in red silk satin, embroidered in gold, silver and polychrome silks
106,5 x 177 cm
Inv. MT. 199

liturgy, promoting, in harmony with the gilt woodwork and inset stones in marble of the chapels, an atmosphere of great baroque theatricality. Equal testimony is given to the objects used in liturgical ceremonies, through the presentation of nationally made 18th century chalices, as well as a single set of baroque trays which, not being devotional utensils, were only used for decoration on the devotional tables, a practice that has completely disappeared in Portugal. ■

King João III and Queen Catarina of Austria
Cristóvão Lopes
Portugal, 1550-1560
Oil on wood
65 x 50,5 cm
Inv. Pin. 50 and Pin. 51

These two portraits, which constitute a pair, represent João III (1502-1557),
King of Portugal between 1525 and 1557, and his wife, the Queen Catarina
of Austria (1507-1578), daughter of King Filipe I and Joana de Castela,
the Mad, and sister of Emperor Carlos V.
King João III is portrayed in this painting with short hair, thick beard that is
going blonde, wearing a black coat and beret. Queen Catarina of Austria,
is represented richly dressed with a dark velvet dress, embroidered in gold
thread, with a coif on her head, a tiara of pearls and gold and pearl
earrings. It is a replica of the portraits represented by the Flemish Master
António Moro, in 1522 (Museo Nacional del Prado, Madrid), generally
attributed to Cristovão Lopes, son of Gregório Lopes, successor in the role
of royal painter from 1550.
This pair of portraits are of particular importance in the context of the
collection of the Museum of São Roque as they constitute a testimony of the
close connections created between the Portuguese Royal family and the
Society of Jesus, as well as a symbol of the foundation of the Church
and of the Professed House of São Roque.

Saint Ignatius of Loyola and Saint Francis Xavier
Portuguese work with *nambam* influence, c. 1600
Gilt and polychrome wood
113 x 41 x 26 cm and 114 x 52 x 27 cm
Inv. Esc. 93 and Esc. 92

These sculptures, originating from the Church and Professed House of São Roque can be considered the most erudite representations of Saint Ignatius of Loyola and Saint Francis Xavier.

They are delicately sculpted statues with harmonious proportions – which reveal on the one hand, the typical static quality of Portuguese Mannerist style, introduced by the grand French masters settled in Portugal during the fifteen hundreds (Chanterenne, Ruão and Odarte), recovering, on the other hand, the great symbolic and devotional tradition of the Middle Ages The work in gilded wood is characterised by a "cross breed" plastic treatment, with a flagrant influence from Japanese Art, probably being

Saint Ignatius of Loyola　　　　　　Saint Francis Xavier

situated in a Portuguese workshop but with a clear *namban* art influence. Judging by the position of the right hand, the sculpture of Saint Ignatius, in an ascetic and contemplative pose, would have originally supported either a halo with the Sacred Host, the symbol of the Company of Jesus, or the book of "Constitutions" of the Order.

The physiognomy, poorly shaved beard and greenish look of the face, will have been taken from the funerary mask of the Saint, as it was common for the great mentor of the Order to be represented in accordance with his authentic physiognomy after death. The exotic image of Saint Francis Xavier would have originally held a cross, the main attribute of the Apostle of the Orient which became one of the most represented figures in sculpture throughout the mission of the Portuguese of the 17th and 18th centuries.

Architectonic Reliquary of Saint Donatus Martyr
Germany / Hungary, 14th century (final)
Gilt silver and glass
32,2 x 10 cm (base diam.)
Inv. Rl. 280

This piece, originating from Saint Mary Magdalene of Prozony Abbey, in Hungary, constitutes the oldest reliquary of the Church of São Roque, included in the donation of D. João de Borgia.

The cylindrical display, of medieval characteristics stands upon a hexagonal foot decorated with birds/dragons on its top. This format allowed the faithful to appreciate the relic from all round the piece. Above the base six semicircular lobes emerge, forming the stem; a central knuckle with reliefs imitating the precious inset stones.

Inside the glass showcase, reinforced by three narrow bands of silver, there is a relic of Saint Donatus, Martyr.

At the top there is a cupola, compartmentalised into six faces, with worked edges, that finishes in moulded pinnacle.

Our Lady with the Infant Jesus, Halo and Reliquary
Germany, Regensburg, 16th century (sculpture);
17th century (halo and reliquary)
Chiselled and gilt silver
Our Lady with the Infant Jesus: 34 x 16,3 cm (base diam.)
Halo: 46 x 26,4 cm
Base: 22 x 22 x 22 cm
Inv. Or. 215, Or. 92 and Or. 273

The silver sculpture of Our Lady with the Infant Jesus is one of the most emblematic pieces of the collection of reliquaries of the Museum of São Roque. This precious statue, from Regensburg (Germany), was one of the first offers of D. João de Borgia to the Church and Professed House of São Roque in the 16th century.

It is a well chiselled sculpture, alternating the smooth and polished surfaces of the cloak, faces and hands, with the rugged textures of hair and details of the clothes. The expressiveness of the faces, like the representation of the hair, also reveals a certain archaism of the sculpture.

The oval silver halo, in the shape of a radiant sun, is formed by two concentric hoops with interweaving decoration. This aureole does not belong to the original sculpture. It would have been added in the 17th century, judging by its stylistic characteristics and typologies.

The copper gilt cubic base, decorated with inset coloured stones of crystal and bells on the corners, also did not belong to the original sculpture, although the oldest kept inventory of 1698 in the Historical Archive of Santa Casa da Misericórdia de Lisboa makes a reference to it. The base in question contains the relic of Saint Gregory Thaumaturg, one of the most important relics included in the great donation of D. João de Borgia to the Church of São Roque in 1587.

Reliquary Ark of Saint John de Brito
Henrich Mannlich
Germany, Augsburg, 1694-1698
Chiselled and gilt silver, glass and silk
54 x 93 x 42 cm
Inv. Or. 625

This reliquary ark, in the shape of a rectangular coffin, was offered to the
Society of Jesus by King Pedro II, in homage to the martyrdom of the Jesuit
missionary from Lisbon, Saint John de Brito (1647-1693). The piece is
flanked by two indistinct figures of angels, in chiselled silver, with open
wings; it is still elegantly decorated by other angels of smaller dimensions.
The base sits on four feet in chiselled silver, topped by cherubim. On the
front the royal coat of arms of King Pedro II stands out, enamelled and
surrounded by golden spirals, attesting that the origin was the donator.
The lid presents bands of friezes in meticulous low relief silver, representing
scenes of the martyrdom of Saint John de Brito in Orbyur, India, 1663.
On top of the lid a wider low relief stands out with the representation of the
figure of the saint in his normal iconography: Indian tunic, head covered with a
sari, sandals with wooden soles and a shepherd's crook. As there were no relics
inside the ark, due to the fact that the body of the martyr Saint John de Brito
never came to Portugal, the Jesuits of São Roque soon attributed this piece
to a Eucharistic function; thereby the idea of "Agnus Dei" topping the piece,

surrounded by seraphs, could have been added later, under Jesuit initiative, with the aim of transforming the reliquary ark into a Eucharistic tabernacle.

Reliquary of the Holy Thorn of Christ's Crown
Portugal, 1600
Rock crystal, gold and enamels
7,1 x 4,1 cm
Inv. Rl. 1289

Considered today to be a rare testament
of Renaissance jewellery in Portugal, this piece
of small dimensions, contains a relic of the Holy
Thorn mounted in a small crystal bottle with
enamelled gold mountings, datable to about 1600.

Arm Reliquary of Saint John Chrysostom
Portugal, 16th century (final)
Gilt copper, white silver and inset stones
56 x 13,5 cm (base diam.)
Inv. Rl. 282

This piece is one of finest examples of the arm type
of reliquary, containing a relic of Saint John Chrysostom,
Archbishop of Constantinople. The piece sits atop
a round base in silver with embossed decoration based
on circles and godroons in two bodies, respectively
concave and convex. The body of the arm, in copper
gilt, is decorated by means of vegetal spirals in low
relief of mannerist character. The relic is exhibited
through an oval glass display. Eight inset stones of
different colours decorate the surface of the arm.
It is finished with an open hand of evident perfection
and impressive realism.

Reliquary of Annunciation
Italy, 17th century (2nd half)
Ebony, silver and precious stones
87,5 x 50,4 x 33,5 cm
Inv. Rl. 1253

Reliquary of rectangular base, was originally destined to protect two other precious reliquaries: the *Monstrance Reliquary of the True Cross and Holy Thorn* (Inv. Rl. 1290) and a small *reliquary of the Holy Thorn* (Inv. Rl. 1289).
It is an elegant piece of Italian origin, from the 17th century, probably a commission or offer to the Society of Jesus.
This artistic work is profusely decorated with applications in silver, containing inset precious stones of various colours and shapes. Between the first and second body, a row of crux decussata and flowers cover the whole surface. The central body, flanked by Tuscan columns in marble, has a painting of the Annunciation of the Virgin on alabaster at the centre.

Bust-Reliquary of Saint Romuald Abbot
Portugal, 18th century
Gilt and polychrome wood with silver halo
36,8 x 21,4 x 12,3 cm
Inv. Rl. 1104

This reliquary represents the bust of Saint Romuald which sits upon a red book with golden decoration. The interior of the book is golden with stippling forming lozenges. The saint is wearing an alb and cape. Over the grey background a type of vegetal decoration is featured with some dots spread all over the surface. On the chest, both hands show an oval crystal monstrance window which encloses the relic, in whose interior

there is a silver thread. The almost bald head presents a face of serene expression, with a long beard. Over the head there is a halo in silver, formed by a strip of vegetal decoration from which there are eleven lanced rays. On the back of the book a drawer enclosed the *Authentication* of the relic, with the following inscription: "I give to Mr. Romualdo Ant. of the Society of Jesus the relic which this authentic (document) speaks of".

Reliquary-Monstrance of Saint Vincent Martyr, Saint John Francis Regis, Saint Stanislas Kostka and Saint Sebastian Martyr
Silversmith António Gigli
Rome, 18th century
Embossed and chiselled silver and gilt wood
59,4 x 24,7 x 14,6 cm (Rl. 1254 and Rl. 300); 54,1 x 24,8 x 14,6 cm (Rl. 299)
53,5 x 24,9 x 15,4 cm (Or. 291)
Inv. Rl. 1254, Rl. 300, Rl. 299 and Or. 291

Set of four reliquaries of monstrance type, in silver leaf over a wooden framework, with a base of gilt wood. Over it rise two feet in volutes which hold the base of the piece, between two heads of Cherubim. At the centre a cartouche finished off with a shell is featured. The trunk is formed by the balustraded knuckle flanked by two volutes with vegetal decoration. The connection of this with the receptacle is made by means of a cherub. The relic is inserted in a glassed oval space. The edge is decorated with a strip of pearl shapes. Surrounding a baroque decoration are repeated compositional garlands, volutes and

Relicary-Monstrance of Saint Sebastian Martyr

cherubim, all topped by a curved façade over which two angel heads and a cross having an aureole of supported lanced rays.

The typology of these four reliquaries is very similar in type to the Roman reliquaries of the same era which can be found in Palace of Mafra (Inv.ºs 394, 395, 5782, 5783 and 5784) and also almost identical to four reliquaries at the Church of *San Rocco* (Rome) whose decoration follows the same ornamental patterns.

**Adoration of the Mystical Lamb
by the Celestial Court**
Bento Coelho da Silveira
Portugal, c. 1683
Oil on canvas
160 x 284 cm
Inv. Pin. 198

**Adoration of the Mystical Lamb
by the Martyr Saints**
Bento Coelho da Silveira
Portugal, c. 1683
Oil on canvas
159 x 273 cm
Inv. Pin. 197

**Christ in Glory surrounded
by Martyr Saints**
Fernão Gomes
Portugal, c.1590-1600
Oil on canvas
242 x 288 cm
Inv. Pin. 217

**Virgin in Glory
surrounded by Martyr Saints**
Diogo Teixeira
Portugal, c.1590-1600
Oil on canvas
241,5 x 288 cm
Inv. Pin. 214

These large paintings were originally situated on the altars of the Saints and Martyr Saints protecting the precious collection of relics of the Jesuit temple. They were topped by the semi-circular paintings *Adoration of the Mystical Lamb by the Celestial Court* and *Adoration of the Mystical Lamb by the Martyr Saints* by Bento Coelho da Silveira. The paintings served as protection of the reliquaries, being taken out only on very solemn occasions.

The canvas of *Christ in Glory surrounded by Martyr Saints*, by Fernão Gomes (1548-1612), carries special significance from an iconographic point of view, as it served to link between the image and the relics, a connection that had been re-taken and fomented by the Council of Trent (1545-1563). The figure of the triumphant Christ, standing and holding the cross, dominates the scene, and around him, like a big amphitheatre sits, a pleiad of martyr saints.

There, the two pillars of the Church – Saint Peter and Saint Paul – are highlighted, in the foreground and, immediately following, Saint James, and Saint John the Baptist, on the right hand side, Saint Laurence with Saint John the Evangelist, on the left hand side.

The painting *The Virgin in Glory surrounded by Martyr Saints,* commissioned to Diogo Teixeira, demonstrates how the theme of the Celestial Court is important in the iconographic programme of the Society of Jesus, particularly the relevance given to the cult of the Virgin and the Martyrs and its close connection with the devotion of the relics. The painting gives prominence to the crowned Virgin, in the centre, holding in her right hand the lily of purity and in the left, a palm of the martyr, being surrounded by the glory of musical angels. On each side, groups of saints are arranged, in a composition similar to its partner painting, with special relevance for

the Saints Catherine, Apollonia, and Agatha emphasised in the left hand group of the panel, and Saints Barbara, Lucy and Clare, on the right hand side, followed by an uncountable multitude of Virgin Martyrs with stereotyped features.

The painting *Adoration of the Mystical Lamb by the Celestial Court*, by Bento Coelho, reveals a very interesting composition in the involvement of the group of figures to the central Lamb, above all for the progressive gradation of the figures on different planes, thereby giving notable depth to the panel. The representation of the mystic Lamb, surrounded by figures of celestial musicians, is a clear allusion to the Lamb described in the Book of Apocalypse (Ap. 5:6,8), identified with the person of Christ as an innocent sacrificed victim. It was the Society of Jesus who most spread the symbology of the Lamb or "Agnus Dei" in Portugal, a theme very often repeated in Spanish painting from the *siglo de oro* era (Zurbarán, Juan de Roelas, Baltazar Gomes Figueira, Josefa d'Óbidos).

The semi-circular painting *Adoration of the Mystical Lamb by the Martyr Saints* establishes a parallelism with the theme of the symmetrical altar of the other side of the church. This painting, similar in everything to the painting of the same theme on the opposite side, is formed in its entirety by female celestial figures, playing musical instruments.

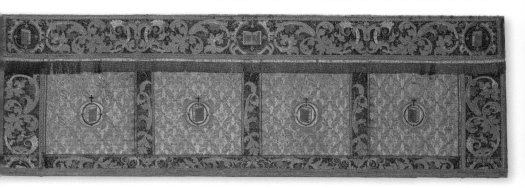

Altar Frontal
Portugal, 17th century
Ground fabric of white silk lamé embroidered in gold, silver and polychrome silk threads
102,5 x 306,5 cm
Inv. MT. 194

The provenance of this altar frontal – Chapel of Our Lady of Doctrine from the Church of São Roque – is identified by the devotional attributes so clear in the embroidery as in the elements of this Chapel, namely the symbol of the Congregation of Our Lady of Doctrine, the Missal and the Rosary. The composition of the frontal is made up of four panels, in the centre of which one can see the Book of Doctrine closed and surrounded by the rosary of Our Lady, serving as the axis of the composition. The panels are made up of a white background, where decoration of embroidered surfaces is laid, whose delicate motifs are associated with the Marian cult – *cartouches* holding the previously cited iconographic motif, rosaries of beads, stars and polylobed floral motifs whose compositional style is identical to the surrounding inlayed marbles in the Chapel of Doctrine.

Armorial Salver
Portugal, 16th century (2nd half)
Embossed and chiselled gilt silver
33 cm (diam.)
Inv. Or. 613

A beautiful example of
armorial salver, standing out
particularly for its heraldic
motif on the central disc – the
coat of arms of D. Francisco da
Gama, Count of Vidigueira,
16th Viceroy of India (1597-1600).
The piece constitutes a good example
of the balance and serenity of the
renaissance period. Associated with the nobility of the material is a rich
game of contrasts of sinuous lines and shapes which achieve an expressive
decoration. The coat of arms acts as a central axis to the three concentric
rings. Following we have a narrow strip with decoration of *cabochons*,
followed by a wider godrooned surface and, finally, a wavy border which
contains a circle of *cartouches*.

Salver
Portugal, Lisbon, 17th century
Embossed and chiselled silver
24,5 x 40 cm
Inv. Or. 617

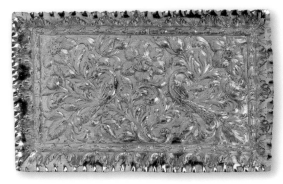

Rectangular salver profusely
decorated with vegetal
motifs. The central part
shows, in low relief, foliage
and flowers of great
corporeality. A central flower divides the surface in two
perfect symmetrical parts. On both the sides there are two peacocks,
in symmetrical positions, this element of presumable oriental influence.
The scene is framed in the foreground, by a narrow band with stylisation

of acanthus, in lower relief, and a wavy border formed by a continuous series of leaves, alternating with fine branches executed in stippling.

Ewer and Basin
Silversmith V.B.
Portugal, Lisbon, c. 1720
Embossed and chiselled silver
Basin: 49 cm (diam.)
Ewer: 33,2 x 17,3 x 12 cm
Inv. Or. 615 and Or. 616

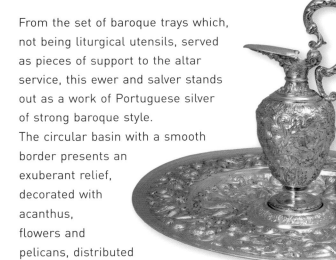

From the set of baroque trays which, not being liturgical utensils, served as pieces of support to the altar service, this ewer and salver stands out as a work of Portuguese silver of strong baroque style.
The circular basin with a smooth border presents an exuberant relief, decorated with acanthus, flowers and pelicans, distributed in two concentric zones, the interior being at a lower level. The central medallion, made up of a big round flower, is surrounded by a fine edge equally of vegetal nature.
The interior part is for the ewer to stand in, in amphora shape profusely decorated with palmettes, rolls of acanthus leaves and flowers. The bulge of the jug is totally embellished with naturalist decoration.
The presence of motifs with pelicans, which have a Eucharistic symbology, suggest the piece had a liturgical destiny, namely functions of washing.

Chalice
Portugal, 18th century (2nd quarter)
Embossed and chiselled gilt silver
28 x 16 cm (base diam.)
Inv. Or. 623

Despite being executed in Portugal and by Portuguese
silversmiths, this piece presents a very clear influence
of Rome, the most powerful and influential centre in
the fabrication of religious utensils in the 18th century,
and also the most important supplier of the Portuguese
court, at the time of King João V.
The decoration shows a heavy relief over a base
of elements of baroque style, such as foliage,
volutes and shells. Over the base three allegoric
female figures are fitting: Faith, Hope and
Charity, from where a false cup of silver emerges
decorating the smooth golden cup. The external decoration of the cup is
formed by a group of flying angels, between clouds and cherubs, holding
instruments of the Passion of Christ.

Christ's Prayer in the Mount of Olives and Washing the Feet Ceremony
Simão Rodrigues and Domingos Vieira Serrão
Portugal, 1600-1610
Oil on wood
176 x 178 cm and 173,5 x 174,5 cm
Inv. Pin. 218 and Pin. 213

The two paintings *Christ's prayer in the Mount of Olives* and *Washing
the Feet Ceremony* would have belonged to a wider cycle of scenes in the
Life and the Passion of Christ, compositions inspired by Flemish engravings
by Hieronimus Wierix for the *Evangelicae Historiae Imagines,* by Father
Jerómino Nadal's authorship – a reference book for the fathers of the
Society of Jesus, which constituted a complete repertoire of images of the
Sacred History. These two panels will have been commissioned by the
Jesuits to the two Mannerist painters Simão Rodrigues and Domingos Vieira
Serrão. There we have two perfect examples of late mannerist painting –

Christ's Prayer
in the Mount of Olives

Washing the Feet
Ceremony

a contained art, in the gestures and in the forms, denoting a correct and purified style in the conception of the scenes, characteristics which were considered fundamental in post-Trento painting.

The painting *Washing the Feet Ceremony* presents an indoor scene, of architectonic background, in which there are thirteen figures: in the foreground: Christ trying to wash the feet of Peter who, apparently, resists; next to Peter is John and the rest of the apostles, without identifying elements, who are in the background of the composition, ending with the figure of Judas, identified by his attribute: a money bag. Note the stylistic similarities between the foot washing basin and the basin of smooth silver used in the Washing of the feet ceremonies of the Church of São Roque, on exhibition in the museum (Inv. Or. 621).

The painting *Christ in the Mount of Olives* takes place outdoors, more concretely in the Mount of Olives. This scene is composed of six identifiable figures. In the foreground, in the middle, the consoling angel next to Christ is emphasised, both invaded by a cloud of light, which symbolically represents the presence of God the Father. On the right, marking the second plane, the apostles sons of Zebedee, John and James, and Saint Peter with a sword. On the left, on the third plane, the figure of Judas following a priest of Sanhedrin and various figures representing Roman soldiers.

Madonna del Popolo
Portugal, 16th century (last quarter)
Oil on wood
145 x 109 cm
Inv. Pin. 32

The devotion to *Madonna del Popolo* was widely spread within the context of the Counter-Reformation, a tendency to which the Jesuits of São Roque did not demonstrate indifference. This veneration is proved to us through the paintings copied from the model which are found in the *Capella Borghese* of Saint Mary Maggiore Basilica, in Rome, traditionally attributed to Saint Luke, assumed as the true portrait of the Virgin.

The devotion to *Madonna del Popolo* will have increased significantly in the 16th century; this devotion prompted the reproduction of this icon, whose replications were exported and spread throughout Christendom. An example

of this is its presence in nearly all the Jesuit houses and missions spread around the world.

In São Roque, we know of at least four replicas, of which, apart from this one, a canvas (Inv. Pin. 127) still remains. One of the referred paintings, today missing, was brought from Rome, in 1569, and offered to Queen Catarina of Austria by Saint Francis Borgia, Father Inácio de Azevedo being the transporter. This model started an intense production of images, characterised by strong formal and emotive contention which reminds us of the *Madonnas* of Christian Medieval and Renaissance art.

the Flemish school, which sought to value the communicative capacity of this type of images.

The piece stands atop a later pedestal, of pyramidal shape, in gilt wood. The existence of this image, in the Church of São Roque, is referenced in a manuscript dated 8 November 1594, as well as in *Relacção de Relicários da Colecção de D. João de Borja, in the Church of São Roque,* documented in 1636, and in the Inventory of the Church and Sacristy of São Roque of 1698, on which this piece is described in the list of attached images of the Chapel of Holy Martyrs. Thus, its initial function as reliquary sculpture is reported.

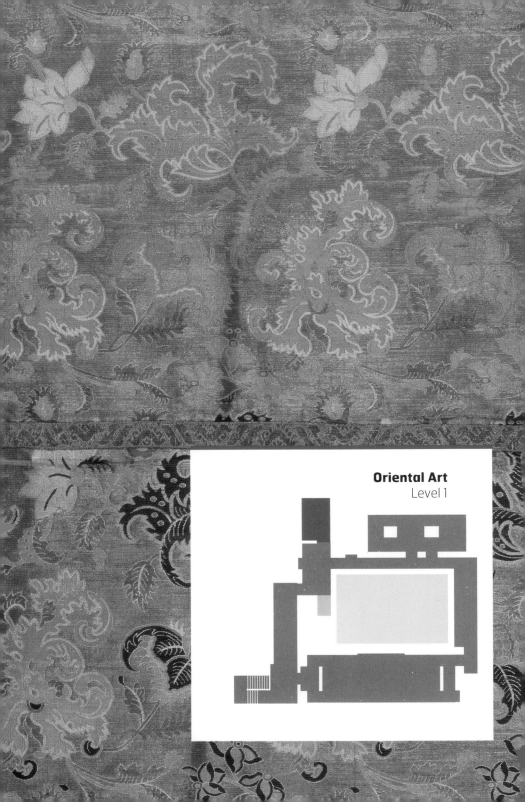

Oriental Art
Level 1

With the arrival to India via ocean routes, in 1498, new ways were opened for the Portuguese economy and for missionary expansion, which had important repercussions in the cultural and artistic plane. The vast territory which made up the Portuguese Orient became an important stage of occurrences which, on the evangelical and cultural level, placed the Society of Jesus in the foreground.

The missionaries of the Society of Jesus were distinct in the way they developed their catechetical action. Conscious of the need of acceptance on the part of the oriental civilisations, they studied the local cultures and religions, bringing together knowledge which allowed them to understand these same civilisations and refute their millennial beliefs.

The cultural contacts established with the local populations by means of missionary actions had important consequences in the field of religious art, seeing the integration of Oriental decorative models, techniques and shapes and, even more rarely, the adoption of shapes copied from Oriental art. This phenomenon, which was felt in the most diverse artistic mediums, gave rise to a renewal of Christian art, as exemplified in the collection of religious art objects exhibited in the museum, a great deal of which came from the Church and Jesuit Professed House of São Roque. Ivory, mother of pearl, silk, lacquered wood and turtle shell, are some of the materials used in the creation of the pieces of this section, which formally follow Western models. Even though it is essentially made up of pieces which belonged to the Society of Jesus, this section dedicated to Oriental Art also

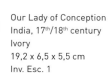

Our Lady of Conception
India, 17th/18th century
Ivory
19,2 x 6,5 x 5,5 cm
Inv. Esc. 1

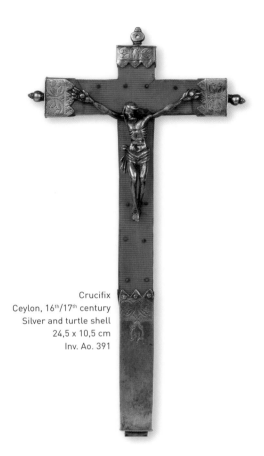

Crucifix
Ceylon, 16th/17th century
Silver and turtle shell
24,5 x 10,5 cm
Inv. Ao. 391

includes works acquired by Santa Casa da Misericórdia de Lisboa or from bequests to the Institution.

The exhibition is organised according to a geographic sequence, such that the pieces are grouped according to their place of fabrication – Near East, India, China and Japan. ■

Reliquary-Cross
Near East (?), 17th century (2nd half)
Wood, mother of pearl, rock crystal
22 x 8,5 x 4,5 cm
Inv. Rl. 276

Wooden pectoral cross, holding on the front
and back fourteen boxes of oval shape in crystal
in which the relics are kept. The cross sits upon
an interesting trapezoidal pedestal (probably added
later) which has inlays of mother of pearl with
floral motifs engraved in black on the front. In the
centre, one can see a miniature parchment
representing Veronica.

In the Near East the production of ornamental
works with applications of mother of pearl was
abundant, as souvenirs for the pilgrimages to the
Holy Land. The iconography of pieces with this
provenance is intimately connected to the Order of Saint Francis and to the
symbols of the Cross of the Holy Sepulchre, which is explained by Saint
Francis of Assisi's relocation to Jerusalem, moved by the need to worship
and live the example of Christ in his home land. Through this Religious
Order it was possible to keep the relations between the Church
and Jerusalem, which brought us valuable testaments of embodied Faith
in pieces such as this.

Reliquary-Casket
India, 16th century (last quarter)
Turtle shell and silver
14 x 21 x 13 cm
Inv. Rl. 1041

Turtle shell casket in the shape of an urn with applications of engraved silver
with *ferroneries* and naturalist motifs, thereby giving originality to this small
casket in its formal simplicity. The use of silver is reduced to the minimum,
limited to the hinges, the tongue and lock, which gives it a modern look,
however being characterised by a perfected technique of soldering of the

various turtle shell plates forming
homogenous and later polished surfaces.
These caskets or "turtle boxes" were
used to guard jewels and valuables, or in
the churches, as ciboria, or even to guard
saint's relics, such as in this case.
Sometimes they preserved the Sacred Host on the
Good Friday celebration.
According to the documentation we referred to, it is one of the oldest Indian
objects exported from India to Portugal, having been received in the Church
of São Roque in Lisbon before 1588, and it may have been offered to the
Church of São Roque by a Jesuit or a benefactor who came from India.

Crucified Christ
Ceylon, 16th century
**Ivory with scarce traces of
polychrome**
45 x 45 x 9 cm
Inv. Esc. 141

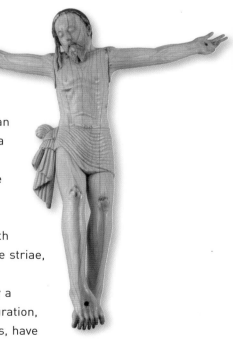

Statue in ivory of Crucified Christ, with an
elongated facial configuration, showing a
closed mouth, a thin nose and wide and
rounded forehead which funnels into the
angular bifurcation of the beard. The
oriental shape of the eyes is curious, a
characteristic which loads the statue with
exoticism. The hair and beard, fall in fine striae,
showing traces of polychrome.
Sculptures of this type, characterised by a
narrow and longilinear anatomic configuration,
with stiff muscles and sticking out bones, have
been classified as Ceylonese-Portuguese.
The Portuguese presence in Ceylon had a great impact on local decorative
arts, as Ceylonese society had a long tradition in this field, having reached
the European market, and particularly the Portuguese. An extensive variety

of works, numerous statues in crystal, safes and counters, stand out as well as Christs and plaque of relief ivory, which are the more important pieces that they made.

This sculpture belongs to the group of the oldest they made, having followed the model of the first sculptures which were on the Portuguese Armadas to the Orient, most probably, late gothic.

Crucified Christ
India, 17th century (final)
Ivory
117 x 59,2 x 15,5 cm
Inv. Esc. 112

This sculpture, of the agonised Christ, is one of the rarest specimens known within the intense production of ivory sculpture made in Portuguese India. It follows the model of the peninsular statutes meanwhile sent to the colonies and later copied by local craftsmen.
In all, it has great anatomical perfection.
Of note are the big dimensions of the piece whose curved axis precisely obeys the shape of the tusk of the elephant from which it originated. Of special note is the detail with which some anatomic features, such as the fine, red outlined mouth, the teeth, the tongue, the eyebrows and the elongated narrow nose, whose exoticism is concentrated, essentially, in the expression of the big and almond shaped eyes.
According to an old description, this statue came from the sacristy of the Convent of São Pedro de Alcântara, constructed in 1680 under the initiative of D. António Luís de Menezes, Marquis of Marialva, Count of Cantanhede, with a view to housing the monks of the Order of Santa Maria da Arrábida, building that was handed over to Misericórdia de Lisboa in 1833, after the secularisation that resulted from the extinction of religious orders.

Chest on a Stand
China, Macao (?), 17th century (chest); 1875 (stand)
Flanders pine wood, resin, inlays of mother of pearl
and metallic fittings
87 x 122 x 70,5 cm (chest)
94 x 123 x 71 cm (stand)
Inv. Ao. 328

Lacquered chest of
parallelpiped shape with
a smooth removable lid,
front and side bands in
resin, filled with inlays
of mother of pearl
supported by feet in the
shape of Chinese dragon.
The front is
compartmentalised in five
sections of rectangular
format, where botanic and
naturalist decorations are
engraved, developing
landscapes with floral
branches, birds and
pagodas, landscaped
backgrounds with houses
in a style characteristic of Japanese painting.
Studies carried out recently point to a possible Chinese origin of the
piece, judging by its density of *cartouche* decoration, a characteristic
which was not very common in Japanese workshops, as well as by the
rest of the decorative typology, like the set of rocks of the front
cartouche on the right, which has more similarities with contemporary
Chinese than with Japanese. This piece could have been made by
Christian Japanese converted to Christianity, who were refugees in
Macau and ended up influencing the local arts, as the façade of
São Paulo attests, where we can still admire various Japanese elements.
Not all the surface dates from the era in which the chest was conceived.

The sides, the upper front area to the upper level of the drawers as well as the respective central face until the upper strip were from the 17th century. From a later time is all the area of the back, the lid and the lower area where the feet stand. In order for the chest to be on a stand, which was appended to it, these elements would have probably been introduced at the start of the 20th century. Of note are the zig-zags which are engraved in many of the frames that are not in mother of pearl but are painted.

The stand which serves as a support, was executed *a posteriori*. On the back the inscription reads: *"G. Ferreira. Pintou. anno 1875 Officina Rª. dos Cordoeiros Lxª"* (G. Ferreira. Painted. Year 1875 Rª. dos Cordoeiros Workshop, Lisbon).

Reliquary-Monstrance
China, Macao (?), 17th century
Embossed and chiselled silver and glass
39,5 x 18,1 x 12,5 cm
Inv. Rl. 60

This reliquary features as one of the most interesting and uncommon pieces of oriental art. In fact its structure is markedly European, characterised by a truncated square base, and aureole around the reliquaries, typical of a 17th century monstrance. The exoticism of the decoration is evident particularly in the irregular rays, in the shape of scales, and in the spheres of identical shape situated on the base and on the knuckle.

The piece sits on a conical square base finished by a boss; from here the stem ascends, in strangely triangular shape, topped by two circular bodies with striae in helicoidal arrangement.

The aureole is made up of forty one rays, which surround ten oval receptacles for relics, one larger central and ten smaller ones around it. This group is topped by a Latin cross, with trilobal ends.

Dalmatic
China, 17th century (2nd half)
Figured taqueté in polychrome silks
and gold wrapped threads
116 cm x 134 cm
Inv. MT. 135

This dalmatic belongs to the Vestments for High Mass, the said *Oriental Vestment*, constituting ten pieces, whose richly exuberantly decorated material is identical in all of them. This material is characterised by an integrally figured *taqueté* and polychrome silks of rich chromaticism with a luxurious and involving composition, vegetal decorative motifs, stylisation of fruit, exotic flowers and lobed flowers and serrated leaves with coils.

The dalmatic is a piece of liturgical clothing included in the group made up of amice, alb, cincture, maniple and stole destined for the ecclesiastical categories of the deacons of the Catholic Church. From the knowledge which has existed since its first use, in the 14th century, the dalmatic would have been called "*levitonarium*", as it was used by the Levites or deacons. Initially its shape had a body and quite long sleeves which became narrower from the 11th century, with slight cuts on the sides for comfort. In the Gothic period the openings prolonged to the armholes, finally having complete side openings, as well as in the sleeves, in the 16th century. The current shape is slightly adopted from the 18th century.

Pots
China, Qing Dinasty (1644-1911), Kangxi period, 17th century (2nd half)
White porcelain decorated in blue cobalt underglaze
33 x 28 cm
Inv. Ao. 1283 and Ao. 1284

We owe to the Society of Jesus and other religious congregations the commission of a series of Chinese porcelain pieces, displaying the respective insignias, for liturgical and daily use in the monasteries. Such is the case of "blue and white" pots, probably made to hold wine or oil, which combine the monogram IHS with floral motifs produced at the end of the Ming dynasty.

Although they do not have any insignia or religious symbology, these "blue and white" Chinese porcelain pots, from the Kangxi period, can be included in this typology, even though dated slightly later, already in the transition of the middle to the end of the 17th century.

The decoration of these pots is painted in cobalt blue underglaze with branches arranged in a continuous spiral of stylised lotus flowers around the body a symbolic element frequently present in the decoration of Chinese crockery, given its close link to Buddhism. The neck is filled in with a row of pointed leaves. They originally had lids.

Tea Service "Saint Ignatius of Loyola"
China, Qing Dynasty (1644-1911), Qianlong period, c. 1750
White porcelain decorated in *grisaille* and gold
Tea cup – 4 x 7,5 cm (diam.)
Saucer – 11,7 cm (diam.)
Tea jar – 13 cm (high)
Hexagonal trays: 13,5 x 13,5 cm and 13 x 8,7 cm

This rare set of pieces, constituting a tea jar, cup and saucer and two small trays in chinese porcelain, densely decorated in *grisaille* (chinese ink) and gold, makes up part of a tea service, along with a teapot and sugar bowl, which is known from other collections.

All the pieces have the same representation of the portrait of Saint Ignatius of Loyola, founder of the Society of Jesus and would have been made to commemorate the bicentenary of the founding of the Order in 1740 and commissioned for a French, Portuguese or Spanish market.

The porcelain, with Christian scenes taken from the Bible, were essentially adapted for the tea services, large dishes and dinner services and mugs, sold as curiosities to a secular market with the intention of honouring the missionary activities in the East, like the importance of the Society of Jesus in the Orient, and consequent influence in China in the 17th and 18th centuries.

Tray
Inv. Ao. 45

Tray
Inv. Ao. 46

Tea jar
Inv. Ao. 42

Saucer
Inv. Ao. 44

Tea cup
Inv. Ao. 43

Saint Ignatius is represented in a posture of blessing with his head surrounded by a traditional halo, with a moustache and oblique Chinese Eyes; holding an open book, over an altar with the Jesuit *motto* AD MAJOREM DEI GLORIAM. Next to the book is an inkpot with a quill and, above these, in the clouds is the Sacred monogram IHS. The iconographic source for this portrait is surely the Schelte A. Bolswert (c. 1581-1659) engraving, "Saint Ignatius of Loyola and Saint Francis Xavier considering the name of Jesus", dated 1622, and opened through a Peter Paul Rubens painting, which would have exerted critical influence on counter-reformist art.

Pieces belonging to this service are found dispersed in museums and private collections, in Europe and in the USA.

Reliquary-Casket
Japan, 16th century (final of the Momoyama period)
Lacquered wood, gold and silver dust (*maqui-é*),
mother of pearl and gilt copper
13,2 x 23 x 15,2 cm
Inv. Rl. 272

This casket, showing polylobed *cartouches* with vegetal elements, is wholly decorated with inlays of mother of pearl (*raden*) over black resin, unusually decorated with gold, thus creating a suggestive polychrome. It is distinguished, not only for its formal beauty, but also for its origins, as it is an old donation to the Professed House of the Society of Jesus.

The survival of a considerable number of small *namban* caskets in Portugal was essentially owed to their reutilisation for the Christian devotion as a reliquary or urn for the Sacred Host. The originality of this example essentially resides in its dimensions as a piece, which, on the other hand, came to justify its use as an object of devotion within the counter-reformed Catholic Church.

One can find various models of this type in Portuguese museums and European private collections, used as much in the lay world as the religious, having been used in great quantity in other areas of the Indies as objects of exchange or offer.

Chapel of Saint John the Baptist

Level 1

The Chapel of Saint John the Baptist constitutes one of the most publicised comissions of King João V (1707-1750), a monarch keen in presenting, through an ambitious cultural programme, the image of a renewed and refined State, in which nothing would be behind the main powers of Europe at the time. So, King João V promoted a vast programme of commissions for grandiose architectonic projects and works of art, amongst which is this chapel.

In fact, although the splendour allowed by gold from Brazil was frequently associated with the reign of King João V, from the 20's, particularly in the 30's and 40's symptoms of economic, social and political crisis emerged in Portugal. The increase of contraband gold from Brazil, difficulties in the Portuguese territories in the East, insubordination of the nobles and decreasing conventual discipline, would, simultaneously, be causes and symptoms of this crisis and of the fragility of political -administrative organisation of the State. The fact that King João V had fallen ill in 1740 and his minister Cardinal da Mota had died in 1747 made this situation worse.

The commission of works of art, in particular architectural works, had a significance in the context of a political instrument of affirmation of the Portuguese state and its monarch, with the aim of giving it the role of European political mediator and, in this way, assuring the hegemony of Portugal, a clearly Atlantic Portugal. To achieve its political objectives, King João V chose Roman baroque as the official architectonic style with classic lines, rejecting painted tiles and gilt woodwork. In order to realise this style he was supported by Ludovice (1670-1752), goldsmith and architect, from Hohenhart (Germany), who had worked in Rome, for the Society of Jesus, before coming to Portugal.

It is in this context that one must understand the commission, in 1742, of the Chapel of Saint John the Baptist to two prestigious Italian architects, Luigi Vanvitelli and Nicola Salvi, which would be built in Rome, between 1742 and 1747, by some of the best artists of the time in accordance with a strict architectural and aesthetic program that included, besides the chapel, liturgical pieces, metalwork and vestments. The architectonic project of the Italian duo, which was closely followed by the Portuguese Court, was subject to alterations suggested by Ludovice with the aim of giving it a more classical feel.

Faced with the possibility of recreating the atmosphere of the Chapel of Saint John the Baptist in the space of the museum, a scheme of exhibiting alternating liturgical vestments.

This collection, unique in the world for its quality of design and composition and richness of the materials used, is made up of a set of embroidered pieces, in silk or gold, which include three different sets:

— Vestments for the **solemn mass**, in silver lamé embroidered in gold thread, in two liturgical colours: red (27 pieces) and white (34 pieces);

— **Festive** vestments in silver lamé embroidered in gold in five colours: red (7 pieces), white (6 pieces), purple (16 pieces), green (9 pieces) and pink (9 pieces);

— Vestments for **quotidian use**, in silk grosgrain embroidered in silk, in five liturgical colours: red (9 pieces), white (9 pieces), purple (9 pieces), green (9 pieces) and black (9 pieces).

The pieces of white ecclesiastical clothing which made up part of the set of vestments – albs, surplices, altar towels, amices, communion burses, chalices veils and manuterges – were decorated with bobbin lace, which are equally exhibited in this section of the museum. This lace follows the technique typologies of Flemish schools, whose origin of fabrication is more complex to define, given the scarcity of the documentation about them which survives today. However, everything indicates that a small number of pieces – the lace of the surplices – would have been of genuine Italian production, most having been produced in Flanders or in the Flemish schools settled in Italy.

Finally, amongst the set of illustrated liturgical books, with engravings created with burins by Flemish and Italian engravers, we feature the *Missale Romanum ex Decreto Sacrosancti Concilii Tridenti restitutum S. Pii V*, printed in Vatican Typography and dated 1735. ■

Model of the Chapel of Saint John the Baptist
Giuseppe Palms, Giuseppe Fochetti, Giuseppe Voyet and Genaro Nicoletti
Italy, Rome, 1744-1747
Polychrome and gilt walnut; painting on copper
140 x 93 x 86 cm
Inv. 326

The model of the Chapel of Saint John the Baptist was conceived in 1743, in the context of the royal commission of King João V to Rome. This piece, which is particularly rare in Portugal, is a testament of the introduction to our country of a way of conceiving the architectural project in successive phases of maturity, outlined by the provisions of academic teaching. Defined by the architect Luigi Vanvitelli (1700-73), after alterations imposed by the Portuguese Court on the original design, its execution was entrusted to the cabinetmaker Giuseppe Palmes. Giuseppe Focheti and Giuseppe Voyet carried out the painting imitating marble. In his turn, Gennaro Nicoletti painted the miniatures of the oil paintings on copper. According to Friar Cláudio da Conceição, chronicler of the kingdom,
this model was delivered to Ludovice, architect of the work of Mafra who had accompanied the construction of the Chapel of Saint John the Baptist. Sousa Viterbo, tells us that this piece, which was kept for many years in the Ludovice family, was given to the *Museu Nacional de Belas Artes* (National Museum of Fine Arts) in 1882. Due to its poor state, it was restored in 1879 by Diodato Guedes and Sebastião Ferreira d'Almeida. In the same year, the *Museu Nacional de Belas Artes* asked for authorisation from the then *Provedor* of Santa Casa da Misericórdia de Lisboa for the painter Silva Porto, from the same Academy, to visit the Chapel *in loco* with the aim of viewing the mosaic pictures, seeing as he was to restore those of the model. It is known today that Sebastião Ferreira d'Almeida painted the two side paintings of the model and Silva Porto, the central painting.
In 1892, Santa Casa da Misericórdia de Lisboa received administrative possession of the Chapel of Saint John the Baptist from the Royal House. In the context of inauguration of the *Museum of the Treasure of the Chapel of St. John the Baptist*, in 1905, the model was acquired by Santa Casa, after the *Provedor's* request to the President of the *Academia de Belas-Artes* (Fine Arts Academy), on 8th October, 1904.

Altar Frontal
Silversmith Antonio Arrighi, following models of sculptors Agostino Corsini, for the *Apocalypse* scene, and Bernardino Ludovisi, for the two angels which flank the relief
Italy, Rome, 1744-1750
White silver, embossed and chiselled, gilt bronze, lapis-lazuli
230 x 112 cm
Inv. MPr. 10

For use only on festive days, this altar frontal is flanked by two standing angels, the central panel of the frontal is made up of a relief in which a scene of the *Apocalypse* can be seen – *The Lamb worshipped by the Elders*. This scene is organised, in compositional terms, following a central axis, showing two dynamic groups of figures on the sides developed in low, medium and high relief, from a sculpting point of view. The relief, chiselled in silver, sits upon lapis-lazuli, and is framed by garlands and *putti*.
The author, silversmith Antonio Arrighi (born in Rome in 1687 and holder of the patent of the silversmith of the pontifical city since 1733) is one of the artists who, in the sphere of silversmithering, worked most for Portugal during the reign of King João V, as the payment books of the Portuguese embassy in Rome show.

Pair of Great Candlesticks
Silversmiths Giuseppe Gagliardi and Leandro Gagliardi, following models
of sculptor Giovanni Battista Maini
Italy, Rome, 1749
Gilt silver and gilt bronze, casted and chiselled
285 x 105 x 105 cm
Inv. MPr. 1 and MPr. 2

Pair of great candlesticks of triangular
pyramidal shape. On the base, held by
sitting *titans*, standing on small niches
crowned by domes, feature the sculptures of
the Doctors of the Church: Saint Jerome,
Saint Thomas of Aquinas and Saint Ambrose
(on one of the candlesticks) and Saint Gregory
the Great, Saint Bonaventure and
Saint Augustine (on the other).
The decoration is hybrid, in so far as it is
composed by architectonic elements
(volutes, rows, acroters), as by elements of
vegetal (thistle, laurel and acanthus) and
zoomorphic characteristics; the presence of
putti can equally be made out.
These two monumental candlesticks
were commissioned in 1744, had their
designs sent to Lisbon – to be approved –
in the month of January 1745. On the
30th July of the same year its
payment started.
The great candlesticks, definitively
completed in 1749, were blessed
before being sent to Portugal.

Gospel altar canon   Central altar canon   Epistle altar canon

Altar Canons
Silversmith Antonio Vendetti
Italy, Rome, 1744-1750
White silver and gilt silver, chiselled and engraved
Central altar canon – 49 x 53 x 9,5 cm
Gospel altar canon – 42 x 33 x 6 cm
Epistle altar canon – 42 x 33 x 6 cm
Inv. MPr. 18 (Central altar canon), MPr. 19 (Gospel altar canon), MPr. 20 (Epistle altar canon)

It is precisely due to the action of Saint Charles Borromeo and of his work that the altar canons are present for the first time (initially only one, containing the *Roman Canon,* a compulsory recitation in all masses, as well as texts of the *Credo, Munda cor, Supplices Te rogamos* and *Placeat tibi*) associated with the celebration of Eucharist. In the concrete case of the set of three altar canons of the chapel of Saint John the Baptist, the framing of the text, the central component in the function of the altar canon, is undertaken through a copious decoration in architectonic style. The **central altar canon**, of larger dimensions, has the architrave supported by pilasters, at the centre of which an elliptic shaped medallion can be seen, with a depiction of the institution of Communion, surrounded by representations of the theological virtues (Faith, Hope and Charity). Over the pilasters, symbols of the Pontificate and the Church can be seen. Mirrored on the stems, there are the figurations of Melquisedeque and of Aaron.

The base has lateral supports decorated with angels, which emerge equally as supports of the Portuguese Royal Coat of Arms, arranged at the centre.

of Saint John the Baptist by the silversmith Vincenzo Belli is rounded with bulging wings in the shape of a torso. The body displays decoration consisting of medallions with depiction of Christ and the Virgin, as well as allegories of the Passion and Purity, and of Faith and of Justice.

The remaining ornamentation is made up of rows, garlands and *ovolos*, denoting rococo taste, characteristic of the work of Vincenzo Belli. On the basin, an entagling decoration, of volutes, garlands and *putti* frame the four medallions in which the following scenes figure: *Saint John the Baptist preaching in the Desert, Saint Peter Receiving the Keys, The Miracle of Multiplying Bread* and the *Apparition of the Risen Christ to Mary Magdalene.*

Communion Vase and Bell
Silversmith Antonio Gigli
Italy, Rome, 1744-1750
Chiselled and gilt silver
Communion vase – 36 x 16,4 cm (diam.)
Bell – 21 x 9,2 cm (diam.)
Inv. MPr. 23 (communion vase) and MPr. 25 (bell)

These two pieces – communion vase and bell – make up part of a set of liturgical utensils which include a pair of cruets on an salver, a chalice and a purifier. Effectively they constitute a set, not only from the stylistic point of view or authorship – all were made by the Roman silversmith Antonio Gigli – but also by their function in the Eucharistic celebration.
The communion vase was for keeping the small consecrated hosts to be distributed to the faithful during communion. It was made by Antonio Gigli for the Chapel of Saint John the Baptist, has a base decorated with heads of *putti*, while the knuckle and bowl has a decoration of flowers, volutes,

Communion vase   Bell

wheat-sheaves and bunches of grapes. The lid has identical decoration with coils, punctuated by cherubim heads.

The use of a bell in the liturgical celebration has been known from the 13th century. Its main function was to get the attention of the congregation at particularly important moments. Later its use was also popularised after the communion of the celebrant, in order to call the faithful to receive communion. On this bell, made by Gigli for the Chapel of Saint John the Baptist, the body is decorated with medallions, foliage and shells and the same decorative solutions continue on the handle. It is topped by an angel head.

White Liturgical Vestments for High Mass
Giuliano Saturni (embroiderer), Francesco Giuliani (tailor)
Italy, Rome, 1744-1749
Gros de Tours white silver lamé, embroidered in gold laid stitch and relief (braids, edges, broaches and tassels; bobbin lace in gilt thread (maniples and stoles); coloured stones (mitre), silk thread worked into knit (gloves), ivory white tabby (lining and ribbons)

This set of vestments, composed of thirty four pieces, was used mainly in the magnificent High Masses, the colour white, was used in High Masses of Easter and Christmas, it was also used on the 24th June, the birthday of Saint John the Baptist, to whom the chapel was dedicated, and the day of the king's namesake.

On such occasions, they would hang the splendid door hangings, arrange the covers over the lecterns, completely decorate the pulpit with the respective cover, a beautiful tapestry was placed over the flooring covering it entirely; placed on the altar was the cushion for the missal, the veil over the chalice, and above this, the burse; as if he were in his cathedral, the patriarch, wearing a cope (or the *capa magna*) over the dalmatic and the light silk and undecorated *tunicella* (absent in this set) and his very fine undergarments, used to celebrate sitting on the faldstool, decorated with its richly embroidered covering: buskins and liturgical shoes on his feet and hands in gloves, on his head a mitre auriphrygiata, on his knees the gremial, on his shoulders a stole and on his arm the maniple, in such a way that his whole body was wrapped in silk and gold. Around him were

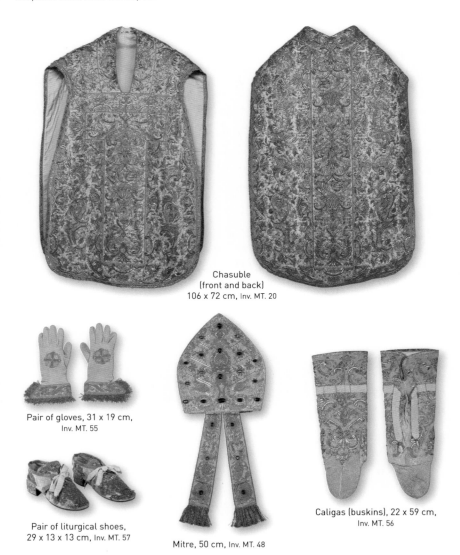

Chasuble
(front and back)
106 x 72 cm, Inv. MT. 20

Pair of gloves, 31 x 19 cm,
Inv. MT. 55

Pair of liturgical shoes,
29 x 13 x 13 cm, Inv. MT. 57

Mitre, 50 cm, Inv. MT. 48

Caligas (buskins), 22 x 59 cm,
Inv. MT. 56

his assistants: the deacon and sub-deacon, respectively with dalmatic
and tunicle, each with a maniple and stole, and six serving canons dressed
in copes.

They were created in Giuliano Saturni's Roman workshop, possibly the
oldest and certainly the most talented of artist embroiderers who worked
for the Lisbon Court, whose activity is found documented from 1712.
The embroidery completely covers all the pieces, yet without being heavy

Altar cushion,
51 x 41 cm, Inv. MT. 40

Chalice veil,
66 x 68 cm, Inv. MT. 97

zig-zag (or spine) motif, over which small floral compositions arranged in an orderly manner following an alternating scheme stand out. The presence of so many sequins gives a particular effect, which make the surface yet more shiny, and have even greater sensitivity to the reflections of light. The complete vestments were attributed to Nicolo Bovi, who is also thought to be the author of vestments ordered by Pope Benedict XIV conserved in the Treasury of the Basilica of Saint Peter of the Vatican, similar in the level of decoration and technique, due to the spine embroidered background, which maybe alludes to Pope Benedict XIV's coat of Arms, and also rich solemn vestments in gold, from the Cathedral of Saint Peter of Bologna, offered by the same Pope Lambertini.

Festive Red Liturgical Vestments
Filippo Salandri (embroiderer), Francesco Giuliani (tailor)
Italy, Rome, 1744-1749
Gros de Tours lamé in gilt silver embroidered in gold; red tabby (linings and ribbons); gilt thread and gilt plate (braids, broaches, fringes and tassels); bobbin lace in gold thread (maniple and stole)

These vestments, composed of seven pieces, were executed by Filippo Salandri. The decoration of the red service destined for festivities, animated by asymmetric *cartouches* and by a profusion interlacing exotic flowers,

Altar frontal, 108 x 225 cm, Inv. MT. 148

Burse,
31,5 x 31,5 cm, Inv. MT. 29

Chalice veil,
77 x 74 cm, Inv. MT. 107

which appear from the coils in the volutes and go in all directions, it is inspired by analogue motifs created for the textiles of the first decades of the seventeen hundreds, which are defined *bizarros,* in which the oriental component (China and Japan) gives the work a quite ostentatious or even eccentric appearance.

Filippo, the active expert master in Salindri's Roman workshop created the red and rose festive vestments for the chapel; Benedetto executed a quotidian green set for the same collection and in 1746, alongside Girolamo Mariani, embroidered two large frontals for the Confession Altar of the Basilica of Saint Peter of the Vatican; Gio Batta in turn created the quotidian red service for the chapel; the works of Carlo Salandri did not reach us.

Festive Green Liturgical Vestments
Filippo Gabrielli (embroiderer), Francesco Giuliani (tailor)
Italy, Rome, 1744-1749
Gros de Tours lamé in gilt silver embroidered in gold; green tabby (linings and ribbons); gilt thread and gilt plate (braids, fringes, broaches and tassels); bobbin lace in gold thread (maniple and stole)

Balanced and static in the development of the decoration, these vestments composed of nine pieces, are particularly pleasing and interesting, above all in reference to the elements of quadrangular shape, such as the door hangings and the chalice veil: on the door hanging, the decoration, which is

Altar frontal, 108 x 225 cm, Inv. MT. 149

Altar cushion,
52 x 40 cm, Inv. MT. 31

Chasuble,
108 x 70 cm, Inv. MT. 23

organised emphasising the perimeter in quite elegant manner, effectively highlights the central composition, which expands from the centre to the edge like a firework. To the contrary, on the chalice veil, meticulously covered with embroidery, floral and geometric motifs converge in the centre, where the monogram IHS is recognisable, surrounded by rays, between which small flowers and loops of twisting vine gracefully wind. Filippo Gabrielli, probably of the same family (maybe son) of Francesco Gabrielli who worked, like Giuliano Saturni, for the Papal Court and for the Portuguese Court from 1714, also created the embroidery for the quotidian purple chasuble, and the larger curtain for Holy Week for the chapel. His ability would not certainly be inferior to that of the older Saturni, who he worked alongside, with Cosimo Paternostro, successfully concluding the works originally commissioned to the master.

Festive Purple Liturgical Vestments
Cosimo Paternostro (embroiderer), Francesco Giuliani (tailor)
Italy, Rome, 1744-1749
Gros de Tours lamé in gilt silver, embroidered in gold; purple tabby (linings and ribbons); gilt thread and gilt plate (braids, fringes, broaches and tassels); bobbin lace in gold thread (maniple and stole)

The festive purple vestments, composed of 10 pieces, conserved in its entirety, include the door hangings as well as the altar frontal. Together with the rose these vestments are perhaps the most refined among the festive sets, for the happy contrast established between the purple background and the gold embroidery. A very rich pastoral stole can be added to this set, destined for administering the sacraments, embroidered on both sides, in purple and white colour (Baptism,

Chasuble, 110 x 71 cm, Inv. MT. 24

Altar cushion,
51 x 41 cm, Inv. MT. 33

Chalice veil,
76 x 75 cm, Inv. MT. 93

white; Penitence etc., purple). Made by Cosimo Paternostro, shows a perfect synthesis between the baroque tradition and rococo exoticism, between linearity and plastic effects: The embroidery of these vestments maintains an extremely high quality in each of its pieces, even those of smaller dimension.

Festive Rose Liturgical Vestments
Filippo Salandri (embroiderer), Francesco Giuliani (tailor)
Italy, Rome, 1744-1749
Gros de Tours lamé in gilt silver, embroidered in gold; rose tabby (linings and ribbons); gilt thread and gilt plate (braids, fringes, broaches and tassels); bobbin lace in gold thread (maniple and stole)

These vestments, composed of nine pieces, were made by Filippo Salandri. Together with the purple these are perhaps the most elegant of the festives, due to the delicate contrast established between the rose background and the embroidery in gold. Even keeping in mind the general unity of the decorative programme, which makes all the festive sets of the textile collection of the chapel of Saint John the Baptist apparently very similar, also these very beautiful vestments find their originality and particular individualisation from a decorative point of view in the variety of details and in its complex articulation. On the altar frontal, for example, there are

Altar frontal, 108 x 225 cm, Inv. MT. 153

Chalice veil,
78 x 75 cm, Inv. MT. 100

Chasuble,
108 x 72 cm, Inv. MT. 25

cartouches which include a series of lace motifs collected in the typical decorations of the materials of French origin from the 1730's. The floral motifs go back to either the *chinoiseries*, or to the more classical, not yet abandoned solutions; a *girandola* of acanthuses together with fringed palms can also be seen.

Quotidian Liturgical Vestments
Carlo (and Margherita?) Abbondio, Gio Batta Salandri,
Benedetto Salandri, Filippo Gabrielli, Nicolo Bovi (embroiderers);
Francesco Giuliani (tailor)
Italy, Rome, 1744-1749
Gros de Tours moiré (grosgrain) embroidered in yellow silk; linings in tabby
in the respective colours; fringes, braids, cords and tassels in yellow silk

In white, red, green, purple and black, each group of this set of vestments,
is composed of nine pieces. It was executed by five different artists,
the quotidian service for the chapel, which survived whole, including the
frontals and the five pairs of door hangings as is indicated in the inventory
of 1784, is a homogenous group in regard to the materials and style, in
perfect harmony with the festive and solemn vestments, in relation to which
it appears as a simplified proposal, for the use of a background fabric that
is less precious but more robust and of great effect – the *gros de Tours
moiré* (*Amuer* in the documents) in place of *lamé* – and of the gold yellow
silk thread for the embroideries, instead of the gold threads. In fact,
the artists followed a common scheme, proposing in its incredible variety
wide ornamental repertoire that encompasses stylised and naturalist
flowers, mixtilinear *cartouches* and geometric forms, shells, volutes, refined

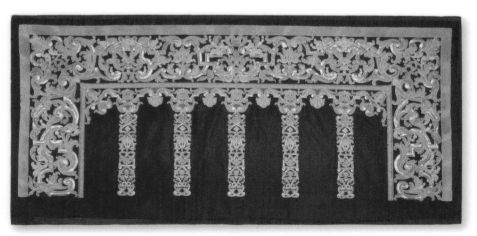

Altar frontal, 108 x 225 cm, Inv. MT. 154

Maniple,
107 x 30 cm, Inv. MT. 102

Chasuble,
108 x 70 cm, Inv. MT. 111

lace motifs, all wisely distributed, be they in the *candelabrum* which decorate the vertical sections of chasubles and frontals, or in the borders that surround the door hangings and chalice veils. From the decorative point of view, this set presents strong analogies with the festive vestments composed of chasubles in the full liturgical colours, donated to the Cathedral of Saint Peter of Bologna, by Pope Benedict XIV circa 1740. In both textile sets, we can see, either in the ornamental solutions of the chasubles or in the inspiration of the embroidered motifs of the frontals, a clear reference to the works of Frederico Nave, reputed artist active in Rome in the first quarter of the 18th century, author of the very beautiful red solemn vestments made for the Church of *Santa Maria della Steccata di Parma*.

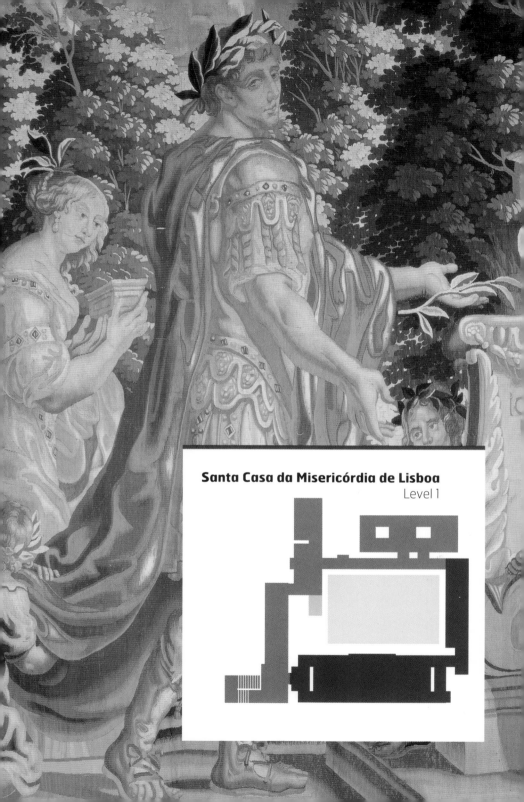

Santa Casa da Misericórdia de Lisboa

Level 1

In 1498, with the King Manuel I (1469-1521) being absent in Castela, D. Leonor (1458-1525), Queen widow of King João II (1455-1495) assumed temporary the reign. It was in this reign that D. Leonor ordered the creation of a brotherhood invoking Our Lady of Mercy (Nossa Senhora da Misericórdia), whose objective was relieve the serious problems of health care in Portugal. In the pursuit of this aim the queen counted on the help of her confessor, Friar Miguel Contreiras (1431-1505), Trinitarium Monk, from Spain, who came to Portugal in 1481, dedicating himself, in particular, to aid and charity.

The Misericórdia de Lisboa chose as its identifying symbol the image of the Virgin Mary with an open cloak, in a protective gesture for all social groups – clergy, nobility and the people – not forgetting groups excluded from society such as the crippled or prisoners, a symbol which visually materialises the mission of the Institution.

The Institution was at first based in the Chapel of Terra-Solta, in the Cathedral of Lisbon, and was later transferred to the Manueline church of Conceição Velha in 1534. With the installations of Misericórdia de Lisboa being destroyed by the earthquake of 1755, and the Society of Jesus being expelled from Portuguese territory in 1759, King José I (1714-1777) donated the Church and Professed House of São Roque to the aforementioned Institution, which moved there in 1768, where it has stayed until today.

From the date of its foundation, Santa Casa da Misericórdia de Lisboa has had an important role in assistance in Lisbon, its viability, from the financial point of view, coming from support of the Portuguese state and private support, through donations and bequests.

Featured in this context is the concession to the Misericórdia de Lisboa of the annual national lottery, by Queen Maria I in 1783, whose profits were shared in equal parts by the Royal Hospital, the Expostos (Foundlings) and by the Academia Real das Ciências (Royal Academy of Sciences). However, only in 1828 were all raffles draws and lotteries prohibited except those conceded to Santa Casa da Misericórdia de Lisboa and to Casa Pia do Desterro. Throughout the 19th century the working of the Lotaria Nacional (National Lottery) was regularised, increasing in its frequency and intensifying the restrictive and prohibitive measures of other forms of lottery and gambling, including prohibiting the sale of foreign lotteries. In the 20th century, Santa Casa da Misericórdia de Lisboa proceded to create and launch other types of lotteries, such as the *Lotaria Popular* (Popular Lottery) (1987) and the *Lotaria Instantânea* (Instant Lottery) (1995), as well as other social games, like *Totobola* (1961), the *Totoloto* (1985) and Euromillions (2004).

The concession of Social Games to Misericórdia de Lisboa brought national recognition for the importance of the assistance developed by the Institution on behalf of Portuguese society, in particular the most needy. The donations and bequests, namely trusts, make up other forms of expression of this recognition and, simultaneously, finance the assistance of the Institution.

The section of the museum dedicated to the Santa Casa da Misericórdia de Lisboa is intended to make the history of the institution known, depicted by artistic objects with historical and symbolic value such as the painting which represents *The Wedding of Saint Alexis,* in which D. Alvaro da Costa is represented, at the time *Provedor* of the Brotherhood of the Misericórdia de Lisboa, and the *Sceptre of the Provedor,* which in past was used as the insignia of the Misericórdia in the wedding of orphans found by the Institution. Other works deserve equal highlighting, namely the set of Processional Banners of Misericórdia, from the 18th and 19th centuries, commissioned by the *Santa Casa* after its installation in the São Roque complex, and finally the Altar set, consisting of a set of sixteen silver pieces, candlesticks, *palmitos,* altar canons and an altar cross.

The charitable actions of the Portuguese state and individuals to the Misericórdia are also represented in this section by a selection of pieces of higher artistic quality, donated or bequeathed to the Institution. Some of these works originated from buildings with historical and artistic value belonging to the Misericórdia de Lisboa, namely the Franciscan Convent of São Pedro de Alcântara, donated to the Institution in 1833 by King Pedro IV; the old Sanatory of Sant'Ana in Parede, a building by architect Rosendo Carvalheira and bequeathed to the SCML in 1911 by Claudina Chamiço Biester; and a residence in Restelo, bequeathed to the SCML, in 1975, by Enrique Mantero Belard. ■

Our Lady of Mercy (front) and **Our Lady of Piety** (back)
Bernardo Pereira Pegado (front)
Manuel Pereira Pegado (back)
Portugal, 1784
Oil on canvas
87 x 67 cm
Inv. Pin. 30

This is a processional banner of Santa Casa da Misericórdia de Lisboa, composed of one painting representing Our Lady of Mercy (Misericórdia) on the front and another, on the back, representing Our Lady of Piety. Joaquim Caetano, based on a document of the commission of the flag, dated 1784, attributes the front painting to Bernardo Pereira Pegado and the back painting to his nephew, Manuel Pereira Pegado.

Among the four flags of Misericórdia belonging to the collection of Museum of São Roque, this one stands out as a commission on the part Brotherhood of Misericórdia de Lisboa; it coincides historically with the initial period of the settlement of these Brothers in São Roque, after the expulsion of the Society of Jesus from the country.

The iconography of Our Lady of Mercy would have had its origins in a vision of a Benedictine monk, transmitted via tales of Cesário de Heisterbach in 1220-1230, in which Our Lady sheltered a large group of Cistercian monks under an extensive cloak. Nevertheless, some specialists attribute this iconographic model to earlier cultic origins, associating the cloak of the Virgin to the Byzantine veil represented as protector of the empire and the city of Constantinople. The Brotherhood of Misericórdia adopted, from its creation in 1498, the iconographic formula which reveals the Virgin as protector of the different social, religious classes, the royalty and Friar Miguel Contreiras, to whom the creation of Misericórdias is tied.

The representation of Nossa Senhora da Piedade, which became usual on the reverse of banners of the Misericórdias, is securely associated with the intention of preserving the memory of the origin of the Misericórdias, in other words, the Brotherhood of Our Lady of Piety.

Cross and candlesticks

This altar set – made up of six candlesticks, a cross and six *palmitos* faithfully follows the Italian baroque models of the first half of the 18th century, models which were imported from Rome by the Court of King João V. This set with the initials of Casa da Misericórdia de Lisboa is one of the most exceptional works of silver of the end of the 18th century, whose aesthetics already announce the *rocaille*. The extremely high quality of its execution attests to a notable workshop of silversmiths.

The set of **candlesticks**, with a crucifix of the same format at their centre, served as the altar set for the Eucharistic altar. The base, in triple pyramid, is formed by three large angular volutes finished with acanthus and shell decorations. Between these there are monograms of vegetal nature, topped by the Portuguese royal crown, which attests to the royal origin of this precious group of pieces.

Palmitos

The **altar cross** has identical morphology to the altar set candlesticks. The lower part is exactly the same, with a pyramidal base of three feet, central knuckle and quadrangle baluster. From here, the cross of smooth stem is defined, with only a light thread on the borders. At the height of the head of Christ, two halos and the arms of the cross are finished with cherubim surrounded by conchae. Above the Crucified, there is a *cartouche* also in silver with the inscription "INRI" (Iesus Nazarenus Rex Iudeorum = Jesus of Nazareth King of Jews).

The *palmitos*, on which figures the four gospels and the apostles of the Roman Church – Saint Peter and Saint Paul, are arranged alternating between the altar set candlesticks and the crucifix, forming a harmonious set. On the upper part, in a mixed linear space, sitting upon two heads of *putti* and two branches, there is the represented image of a gospel or apostle, of excellent execution.

The use of the **three altar canons** placed on the altar goes back to the post-Tridentine period, constituting a memory aid to the priest during the celebration of the mass in Latin. The altar canons kept their function until the liturgical reform of the Council of the Vatican II (1963-1965).

The **central altar canon**, of larger dimensions than the side ones, generally presents the morphology of a large *cartouche*, wider than it is high, at the centre of which the Roman Canon text and other Mass prayers are written in Latin. On this piece, the frame is made up of elements of *rococo* nature, amongst which stand out conchae and sinuous volutes. In the interior,

Gospel altar canon   Central altar canon   Epistle altar canon

in a rectangular space, the Last Supper is represented, in direct relation
with the text which below reads – The Consecration of Bread: "Hoc est
enim Corpus Meum" and of the Consecration of Wine: "Hic est enim calix
Sanguinis Mei..." Other decorative elements also make allusion to the Body
and Blood of Christ, like the bunches of grapes and wheat sheaves.

The **Epistle altar canon** (right hand side) has the shape of an elongated
cartouche, held by two feet and moulded by pairs of volutes.

The central space in a trapezoid shape with curved sides has within it the
formula of the *Washing*: "*Lavabo inter innocentes*". On top, one can see an
apocalyptic *Agnus Dei*, surrounded by a glory of rays and flanked by a pair
of flying Cherubim.

The **Gospel altar canon** (left hand side) has the same elongated trapezoidal
morphology similar to the previous. The only element that differs is the
upper finishing, this one is made up of an eagle, the main attribute of the
Gospel of Saint John. In the central text the beginning of the Gospel of
Saint John can be read – "*In principio erat Verbum*" – the text that was read
at the end of the celebration of Mass.

Wedding of Saint Alexis
Garcia Fernandes
Portugal, 1541
Oil on wood
210 x 165 cm
Inv. Pin. 54

Until the 20th century, this work, executed in 1541 by Garcia Fernandes, was mistakenly interpreted as a representation of the *Wedding of King Manuel I with D. Leonor*, which took place in 1518, after the death of the monarch's second wife, Infanta D. Maria de Castela. However, in 1998, Joaquim de Oliveira Caetano presented a new interpretation of the work, reading it as portraying representation of the wedding of Saint Alexis.
In fact, it is not plausible for a painting to be commissioned representing the wedding of King Manuel I and D. Leonor twenty three years after this happened. At the time, King Manuel I had died, D. Leonor was in her second marriage to Francisco I of France and the king of Portugal was D. João III, to whom D. Leonor had been promised before marrying King Manuel I. On the other hand, bearing in mind the decrees of Trent, it is unusual to place a work of a profane theme in a sacred religious space. In addition to the fact that the presumed King Manuel I does not present his insignia *Tosão do Ouro* which he would have received in marriage to D. Leonor.
The existence of a Brotherhood of Saint Alexis in the Church of Misericórdia is documented, although we do not know the date of the institution of this Brotherhood. Nevertheless, we know that in 1538 a charitable brotherhood was annexed to the Misericórdia by royal will. Assuming that the brotherhood annexed to the Misericórdia in 1538 was the Brotherhood of Saint Alexis, the execution of a painting dedicated to Saint Alexis in 1542 for placement in the Church of Misericórdia would make sense. It also justifies the presence of the portrait of D. Álvaro da Costa in the painting – identified by an inscription painted on his clothing – seeing as he was the *Provedor* of the Misericórdia in 1538.
In the foreground and at the centre of the composition, the painter represented Saint Alexis, his fiancée and the priest who celebrated the marriage. The figures who attend the ceremony are arranged in a balanced way around the couple, separated by gender. The idealisation

of the faces – in particular of the female faces – , the sinuosity of the bodies and the expressive treatment of the drapery, give a certain grace to the painting.

Offering to the Unknown God
Jan Frans Cornelissen Factory
Flanders, Antwerp, 1662-1678
Polychrome silk, gold and silver threads
388 x 527,5 cm
Inv. MT. 228

A tapestry is a hand woven piece of material to be
hung vertically, in which the design is formed by
woven threads. The images are previously drawn
and painted on cards and then copied onto the
textile. The tapestries were frequently part of a set
of various pieces – the frames. Each piece of
these sets corresponds to a step in a narrative
or decorative cycle.
This artistic medium goes back, in Europe, to at
least the 10th century. From the 13th century and
throughout the 14th and 15th centuries, this art
developed a great deal in the cities of Paris, Arras
and Tournai. In the 16th century, Brussels became
the great European centre of tapestry due to
political and economic changes. With the advent
of the 17th century other important centres of
tapestry production emerged all over Europe,
started by emigrant Flemish artists.
The passage from the Middle Ages to the Modern
era was marked, in the art of tapestry, by a
change in the choice of themes represented,
with emerging themes in addition to the Biblical
episodes and allegories which came from
Medieval tradition, episodes of national
contemporary history and ancient classical
history and mythology.
In accordance with information from Guy Delmarcel, specialist in tapestries,
this piece would have been made in Antwerp, in Jan Frans Cornelissen's
workshop, probably from a card by Flemish painter Abraham van
Diepenbeeck (1596-1675).

Identification of the represented theme is facilitated by reading the inscriptions which appear on the tapestry. On the left hand side, on the top of the border reads "PAX AUG" – *Pax Augusta* –, on the opposite side "VIC. AUG" – *Victoria Augusta*. Still on the border of the tapestry, on the right hand side there is a banner with the motto of Rome: "SPQR" – *Senatus Populusquae romanus* (The Senate and the Roman People). Finally, in the top corners of the border there are two eagles with a crown of laurel, symbol of the Roman Empire.

Equally is the inscription "IGNOTO DEO" (to the Unknown God) on the altar over which the sacred fire burns.

These elements allow the represented scene to be identified: Augustus (63 B.C.-14 A.D.), the first emperor of Rome and responsible for imposing the *Pax Romana* (or Augustus peace), offering devotion to the Unknown God. This cult existed in Ancient Greece and Rome, mentioned in the New Testament, in the book of Acts of the Apostles (Act. 18:22,23) with respect to the evangelical work of Saint Paul in Athens, who associates this Unknown God to the unique God of the Christians.

Augustus is represented at the centre of the composition as general and emperor, with the boots of a Roman officer, the *paludamentum*, or purple cloak, attached at the shoulder with a pin, and a crown of laurel on his head. The Emperor places a branch of laurel on the altar. In front of him a priest holds the *praefericulum* in his left hand, the sacred jar which contained the liquid (wine, milk, honey or blood) of the libation (a devotional action which involved the spilling of a liquid over the altar as an offering to a god). In his right hand, the priest holds the *patena* (plate), another devotional object used in the libation. Around the figures of the Emperor and the priest are other priests and their assistants, two of which are musicians. Following the Emperor is a procession of women and men who carry offerings and torches.

The central composition is surrounded by a baroque border, made up of garlands of flowers and fruits, *cornucopias*, stylised architectonic elements, allegoric figures with olive branches in their hands, arrows and lances and symbolic elements and inscriptions allusive to Rome and Augustus.

In the background there is a landscape with trees and classical architectonic elements.

**Saint Joachim, Saint Anne, Saint Mary Magdalene, Saint Joseph
and Saint John the Baptist**
André Gonçalves
Portugal, c. 1750-1760
Oil on canvas
150 x 92 cm
Inv. Pin. 23, Pin. 24, Pin. 25, Pin. 26 and Pin. 201

A set of five paintings, of identical dimensions, executed by André
Gonçalves, between the years 1750 and 1760. The exhibition of the isolated
figure stripped of attributes and without any historical reference, as well
as large garments of fifteen hundred's suggestion, reveal the neo-classic
sense of André Gonçalves' painting well. The colour, open and bright,
and the framing of the sketched scenery, are also very interesting
characteristics of the painter in this final phase of his work.
The two paintings which present clear attributes are Saint Joseph with the
lily flower, and Saint John the Baptist pointing to the Lamb of God.
José Alberto Gomes Machado puts forward the hypothesis that these
paintings came from the refectory of the Professed House of São Roque,
which would have made them part of the collection that the Misericórdia

| Saint Joachim | Saint Anne | Saint Mary Magdalene |

| Saint Joseph | Saint John the Baptist |

"inherited" from the Society of Jesus, however, no known documentation clearly associates these paintings with the Jesuit headquarters, making it possible that they came to be part of the collection of Santa Casa da Misericórdia de Lisboa by other means.

Imposition of the Rule by Saint Claire
Pedro Alexandrino de Carvalho
Portugal, 18th century (2nd half)
Oil on canvas
250 x 178 cm
Inv. Pin. 256

A painting of clear counter-reformist theme, glorifying the Franciscan mystic of the Congregation of Saint Claire. This large painting of agitated scenic composition reveals the stylistic characteristics of Pedro Alexandrino de Carvalho (1730-1810), the most productive national painter of the second half of the 18th century. It is the only painting of this author in the Museum of São Roque. Here, the painter uses the variety of religious habits to create, in sinuous lines, a painting of great effect, punctuated by wide gestural expressions. The design is presented with correct alacrity, provided

with a smooth colouring, creating a visual effect of great lightness, characteristics of its production.

This painting was incorporated into the collection of the Museum of São Roque, on 9th March, 1984, after its transference from the old building of *Infância Desvalida*, in Lumiar.

Chalice, Paten and Eucharistic Spoon
Jewellers Leitão & Irmão
Portugal, Lisbon, 20th century (early)
Embossed and chiselled gilt silver
Chalice – 30,2 x 15,1 cm (diam. base)
Paten – 16,2 cm (diam.)
Spoon – 9,9 cm
Inv. Or. 865

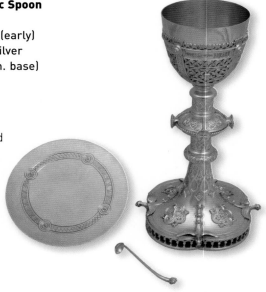

This set of chalice, paten and eucharistic spoon was made for the chapel of the old Sanatorium of Sant'Ana, a building in Parede, which was a project of architect Rosendo Carvalheira that was inaugurated in 1912. These are pieces of high quality metalwork, of elegant and stylised shapes, which denote the influence of Art Nouveau. The refined decoration of the chalice composes geometric and vegetal elements and fantastic animals, related to the Neo-Byzantine style, which is found equally represented in the decorative programme of the chapel of the sanatorium.

The base of the chalice is quadrilobed conical shaped, on each of the four quadrilobes, there is a quatrefoil in relief, two of them with the letter "S" on the interior and a third with the letter "A" – in allusion to the monogram of the sanatorium – and the fourth with a small flower. On top of the cup, an engraved inscription: *"ACCIPITE / ET DIVI/DITE IN/TER VOS"* (Take and share amongst yourselves).

The paten has only one simple decorative element: a band of engraved trefoils, interrupted at four points by buttons with a flower in the interior.
The spoon has a semi-spherical bowl, a curved handle with the head of a fantastic animal, identical to those which appear on the chalice.

Pelican
Portugal, 18th century
Carved and gilt wood
53 x 50 x 26 cm
Inv. Esc. 133

Within Christian symbolism, the
pelican was traditionally seen
as the aquatic bird which fed
its young with its own flesh
and blood, having been adapted,
by Christian iconography, as one
of the symbols of paternal love,
and therefore, of Christ. There is,
therefore, a symbolic association of the
sacrifice of Christ on the cross, with his side open, feeding the church with
his own blood, and thence it appears frequently in the doors of tabernacles,
both painted and in relief.

This interesting work of carved wood, of great originality in the sculpture
collection of Santa Casa da Misericórdia de Lisboa, most probably
originated from the Church of São Pedro de Alcântara, judging by the
initials (IPA) which are inscribed on an old label placed on a small door
which opens on the back of the piece.

Saint Anne and Saint Joachim
Portugal, 18th century
Gilt and polychrome wood
30 x 17 x 10,5 cm and 30,5 x 18 x 10,5 cm
Inv. Esc. 3 and Esc. 2

A pair of sculptures in gilt and polychrome wood, standing on a small
octogonal base outlined with a border imitating marble polychrome.
The image of Saint Anne is densely decorated with stylised and gold
vegetation elements, over a base of red on the tunic and green on the
cloak. Saint Anne is traditionally represented covered by a green cloak
symbolising the transport of hope of the world, and is related with the
devotion of Santa Ana with the belief of the Immaculate Conception of the

Virgin. This devotion is usually associated with the protection of carpenters, ebony workers and lathe workers, also being the representative figure of the *Mother* who teaches catechism, as well as the *Lady of the house* or the patron of family mothers. In this sculpture, the Saint is presented with the traditional hood covering the face, holding in her left hand, the Sacred Book.

The image of Saint Joachim shows interesting golden decorative elements, in contrast with the dark blue of the depths of the clothing and red of the cloak, decorated with wide vegetative elements, characteristic of the seventeen hundreds. The movement and volume of the clothing, of excellent cut, as well as the intense facial expressiveness of the image, combined with the right hand placed on the chest, grant this piece a dramatic Baroque effect.

Saint John the Baptist
Workshop of António Ferreira (?)
Portugal, 18th century (2nd half)
Polychrome terracotta
52 x 36 x 15 cm
Inv. Esc. 145

Representation of the prophet, predecessor of Christ, as a child, iconography which was popularised by the Italian Renaissance and which generally associates Saint John the Baptist with Infant Jesus. The saint is represented here with his traditional attributes, that is, a baptismal shell in his right hand and head leaning on his left hand, while looking at a lamb lying on a tree stump.

The characteristics of the piece, point to the possibility that it is a figure which was once part of a nativity scene from the Lisbon clay master António Ferreira's workshop, a sculptor who was especially admired by other artists of the age, namely Machado de Castro, who ended up creating his own style which would come to influence other Portuguese clay sculptors.

Of note, in this beautiful example, is the stylistic identity of some figures of peasant children in the nativity scene in *Madre de Deus*, in Lisbon, also by António Ferreira, which through the movement and naturalism presented, reflect the baroque mentality of the time.

Saint Augustine of Hippo
Portugal, 18th century
Gilt and polychrome wood
142 x 78 x 42 cm
Inv. Esc. 95

This sculpture of Saint
Augustine of Hippo, strongly
representative of the Baroque
period, of undeniable technical and
artistic quality, is characterised
by intense gestures and dynamic
rhythms in the definition of shapes.
Saint Augustine was bishop of Hippo,
where he would die in 430. The saint
is wearing ecclesiastic outfits, the
wavy creases of which were valued
by a decoration of the seventeen
hundreds, based on exuberant stylised
floral and vegetable elements.
Iconographically, he is represented
with the attire of the bishop, including
a magisterial mitre with green
encrusted stones, a medallion which
closes the hood with a red stone,
red gloves and a book held in his
left hand.

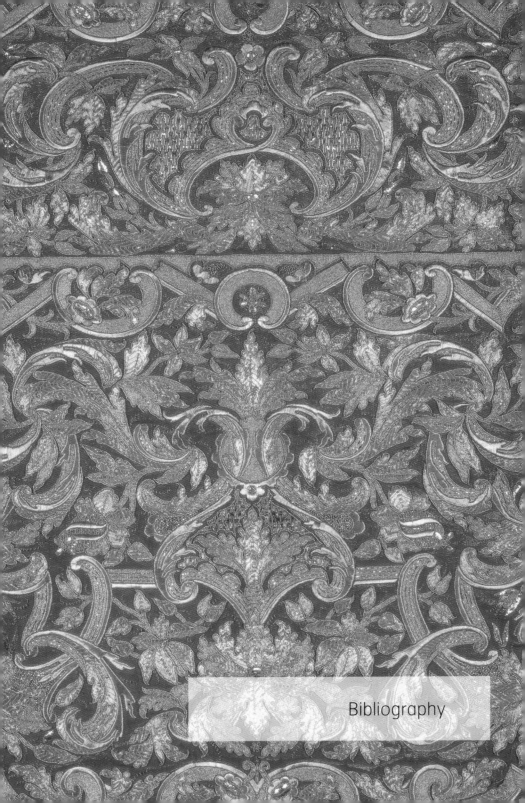

Bibliography

ALARCÃO, Teresa, CARVALHO, José Alberto Seabra, *Imagens em Paramentos Bordados. Séculos XIV a XVI*, Instituto Português de Museus, Lisbon, 1993.

ARRUDA, Luísa, *Hospital de Sant'Ana. 1904-2004. 100 Anos. Sanatório de Sant'Ana*, Santa Casa da Misericórdia de Lisboa, Lisbon, 2004.

BAPTISTA PEREIRA, Fernando António, *História da Arte Portuguesa* (1500-1800), Universidade Aberta, Lisbon, 1992.

BAPTISTA PEREIRA, Fernando António, (coord.), *As Ruínas de S. Paulo, um Monumento para o Futuro*, Instituto Cultural de Macau/Missão de Macau em Lisboa, Lisbon, 1995.

BAPTISTA PEREIRA, Fernando António, *A Arte Portuguesa da Época dos Descobrimentos*, CTT – Correios de Portugal, Lisbon, 1996.

BAPTISTA PEREIRA, Fernando António, COUTINHO, Maria Isabel, FIGUEIREDO, Maria Rosa, (coord.), *A Arte e o Mar*, Fundação Calouste Gulbenkian, Lisbon, 1998.

BAPTISTA PEREIRA, Fernando António, *Imagens e Histórias de devoção. Espaço, tempo e narrativa na Pintura Portuguesa do Renascimento*, Doctoral Dissertation presented in Faculdade de Belas Artes – Universidade de Lisboa, (type-written text), Lisbon, 2001.

BESSONE, Silvana (coord.), *Lisboa Há 100 Anos*, Museu Nacional dos Coches, Instituto Português de Museus, Lisbon, 2005.

BEURDELEY, Michel, *Porcelaine de la Compagnie des Indes,* Office du Livre, Fribourg, 1962.

BEURDELEY, Michel, RANDRE, Guy, *La porcelaine des Qing : «Famille verte» et «Famille rose»*, Office du Livre, Fribourg, 1985.

BOWRON, Edgar Peters, RISHEL, Joseph J., (coord.), *Art in Rome in the Eighteenth Century*, Merrell – Philadelphia Museum of Art, Philadelphia, 2000.

BOYER, Martha, *Japanese Export Lacquer from the Seventeenth century in the National Museum of Denmark*, National Museum of Denmark, Copenhagen, 1959.

BRAZÃO, Eduardo, *D. João V. Subsídios para a história do seu reinado*, Portucalense, Oporto, 1945.

CAETANO, Joaquim Oliveira, (coord.), *Garcia Fernandes. Um pintor do Renascimento Eleitor da Misericórdia de Lisboa*, Santa Casa da Misericórdia de Lisboa/Museu de São Roque, Lisbon, 1998.

CAETANO, Joaquim Oliveira, *Pintura. Século XVI ao Século XX – Colecção de Pintura da Misericórdia de Lisboa*, Tome I and II, Colecção Património Artístico, Histórico e Cultural da Santa Casa da Misericórdia de Lisboa, vol. V, Santa Casa da Misericórdia de Lisboa/Museu de São Roque, Lisbon, 1998.

CALADO, Maria Margarida, *Arte e Sociedade na Época de D. João V*, Doctoral Dissertation in Art History presented in Faculdade de Ciências Sociais e Humanas – Universidade Nova de Lisboa, (type-written text), Lisbon, 1995.

CALDAS, José, *Os Jesuítas e a sua influência na actual sociedade portuguesa: meio de a conjurar*, Lello e Irmão Editores, Oporto, 1901.

CALISSONI, Anna Bulgari, *Maestri Argentieri, Gemmari e Orafi di Roma*, Fratelli Palombi Editori, Rome, 1987.

CAMPOS, Correia, *A Virgem na Arte Nacional*, Tipografia Oficina de S. José, Braga, 1956.

CANDIAGO, Anna, "Un Tesoro di Oreficeria Romana del Secolo XVIII a Lisbona: Gli Argenti di S. Rocco", in *Estudos Italianos em Portugal*, no. 24, Lisbon, 1965, pp. 61-79.

CANEPA, Teresa, *Imagens do Cristianismo na Porcelana da China*, Jorge Welsh – Porcelana Oriental e Obras de Arte, Lisbon/London, 2003.

CELLINI, Antonia Nava, *La Scultura del Settecento*, 2nd edition, Garzanti Editore, Milan, 1992.

CHECA CREMADES, Fernando, (coord.), *Felipe II – Un monarca y su época – Un Principe del Renacimiento*, Museu del Prado, Sociedad Estatal para la Conmemoración de lo Centenário de Felipe II y Carlos V, Madrid, 1999.

CHEVALIER, Jean, GHERBRANT, Alain, *Dicionário de Símbolos*, José Olympio Editora, Rio de Janeiro, 1982.

CID, Jorge, *São Roque e o seu Museu*, Colecção Portugal – A Arte: Os Monumentos: a Paisagem: Os Costumes: As Curiosidades, Portucalense Editora Lda., Barcelos, 1931.

CLODE, Luiza, *Exposição Mariana*, Museu de Arte Sacra, Funchal, 1988.

CORREIA GUEDES, Maria Natália, (coord.), *Encontro de Culturas – Oito séculos de missionação portuguesa*, Conferência Episcopal Portuguesa, Lisbon, 1994.

CORREIA GUEDES, Maria Natália, (coord.), *Fons Vitae – Pavilhão da Santa Sé na Expo' 98*, Lisbon, 1998.

CORREIA GUEDES, Maria Natália, (coord.), *500 Anos das Misericórdias Portuguesas. Solidariedade de Geração em Geração*, Comissão para as Comemorações dos 500 Anos das Misericórdias, Lisbon, 2002.

CORREIA GUEDES, Maria Natália, (coord.), *Thesaurus. Vocabulário de objectos do culto católico*, Fundação da Casa da Bragança, Vila Viçosa, 2004.

COSTA LIMA, Joaquim, "São Roque e os Seus Artistas", in *Revista Municipal*, no. 58, Câmara Municipal de Lisboa, Lisbon, 1953, pp. 5-14.

COSTA, Marisa, "Quatro Tábuas Quinhentistas Dedicadas a São Roque por Devotos Lisboetas", in *ARTIS*, no. 4, Faculdade de Letras da Universidade de Lisboa, Lisbon, 2005, pp. 81-119.

CUNHA, Mafalda Soares da, (coord.), *Os Espaços de um Império*, Museu dos Transportes e Comunicações, Oporto, 1999.

CUNHA, Rosalina Branca da Silva, (coord.), *Os Descobrimentos Portugueses e a Europa do Renascimento – "Cumpriu-se o Mar" – A Arte na Rota do Oriente*, XVII Exposição Europeia de Arte, Ciência e Cultura, Presidência do Conselho de Ministros/Comissariado para a XVII Exposição de Arte, Ciência e Cultura/Imprensa Nacional – Casa da Moeda, Lisbon, 1983.

CUNHA, Rosalina Branca da Silva, (coord.), *Os Descobrimentos Portugueses e a Europa do Renascimento – "O Homem e a Hora são um só" – A Dinastia de Avis*, XVII Exposição Europeia de Arte, Ciência e Cultura, Presidência do Conselho de Ministros/Comissariado para a XVII Exposição de Arte, Ciência e Cultura/Imprensa Nacional – Casa da Moeda, Lisbon, 1983.

Depois dos Bárbaros II – Arte Namban para os Mercados Japonês, Português e Holandês, Jorge Welsh Books – Publishers and Booksellers, London, 2008, pp. 59-60.

Descobrimentos Portugueses e seus Reflexos nas Colecções da Casa de Habsburgo, Kunsthistorisches Museum, Wien, 2001.

DIAS, Pedro, (coord.), *No Tempo das Feitorias. A Arte Portuguesa na Época dos Descobrimentos*, vols. I and II, Comissão Nacional para as Comemorações dos Descobrimentos Portugueses, Lisbon, 1992.

DIAS, Pedro, *A Escultura Maneirista Portuguesa*, Minerva, Coimbra, 1995.

DIAS, Pedro, (coord.), *O Brilho do Norte – Escultura e Escultores do Norte da Europa em Portugal*, Galeria de Pintura do Rei D. Luís, Comissão Nacional para as Comemorações dos Descobrimentos Portugueses, Lisbon, 1997.

DIAS, Pedro, *História da Arte Portuguesa no Mundo (1415-1822)*, vols. I and II, Círculo de Leitores, Lisbon, 1998.

Documentos para a História da Arte em Portugal – Arquivo do Tribunal de Contas – Colégios de Santo Antão, São Roque, São Francisco Xavier e Noviciado de Arroios (Companhia de Jesus), vol. 5, Fundação Calouste Gulbenkian, Lisbon, 1969.

Ermida de São Roque: Resumo histórico da sua origem e da sua irmandade na cidade de Lisboa, Typografia Universal, Lisbon, 1869.

ESPIR, Helen, *European Decoration on Oriental Porcelain, 1700-1830*, Jorge Welsh Books, London, 2005.

ESTEVAM, José, "Relíquias e pinturas da Igreja de S. Roque", in *Revista Municipal*, no. 88, Lisbon, 1961, pp. 55-68.

FALCÃO, José António, REIDEL, Hermann, (coord.), *Rosa Mystica – Nossa Senhora na Arte do Sul de Portugal*, Tesouro da Catedral de Ratisbona, Schnell Steiner, Regensburg, 1999.

FERRÃO, Bernardo, *Mobiliário Português – Índia e Japão*, vol. III, Lello & Irmãos Editores, Oporto, 1990.

FLORES, Jorge, VASSALLO E SILVA, Nuno, (coord.), *Goa e o Grão-Mogol*, Fundação Calouste Gulbenkian, Lisbon, 2004.

FRANÇA, José-Augusto, *O Retrato em Portugal*, Livros Horizonte, Lisbon, 1981.

GARMS, Jörg, "La Capella di S. Giovanni Battista nella Chiesa di S. Rocco a Lisbona", in ROCCA, Sandra Vasco, BORGHINI, Gabriele (dir.), *Giovanni V di Portogallo e la Cultura Romana del suo Tempo*, Àrgos Edizioni, Rome, 1995, pp. 113-123.

FUSCONI, Giulia, *Disegni Decorativi del Barocco Romano*, Edizioni Quasar, Rome, 1986.

HERNMARCK, Carl, *The Art of the European Silversmith (1430-1830)*, vol. II, Sotheby/Parke Bernet, London and New York, 1977.

HERVOÜET, François et Nicole, BRUNEAU, Yves, *La Porcelaine des Compagnies des Indes à Décor Occidental*, Flammarion, Paris, 1989.

Historia dos Mosteiros Conventos e Casas Religiosas de Lisboa, Tome I and II, Oficinas da Gráfica Santelmo, Câmara Municipal de Lisboa, Lisbon, 1920.

HONOUR, Hugh, *Goldsmiths and Silversmiths*, Weidenfedl & Nicholson, London, 1971.

HOWARD, David and AYERS, John, *China for the West: Chinese Porcelain & other decorative arts for export illustrated from the Mottahedeh Collection*, vol. I, Sotheby's Parke Bernet, London and New York, 1978.

IMPEY, Oliver, JÖRG, Christiaan, *Japanese Export Lacquer. 1580-1850*, Hotei Publishing Amsterdam, Amsterdam, 2005.

JORDAN-GSCHWEND, Annemarie, *O retrato de Corte em Portugal*, Quetzal, Lisbon, 1994.

LAMEIRA, Francisco, *O Retábulo da Companhia de Jesus em Portugal: 1619-1759*, Gambelas: Promontória Monográfica História da Arte 02: Universidade do Algarve: Departamento de História, Arqueologia e Património, Faro, 2006.

LAVAGNINO, Emilio, *L'Opera del Genio Italiano all'Estero. Gli Artisti in Portogallo*, La Libreria dello Stato, Rome, 1940.

LEITE, Serafim, "A Capela de S. João Baptista na Igreja de S. Roque" in *Guia de Portugal Artístico*, vol. IV, Livraria Portugália Editora, Lisbon, n.d., pp. 9-24.

LEVENSON, Jay A., (coord.), *Encompassing the Globe – Portugal and the World in the 16th and 17th centuries*, Smithsonian Institution, Ed. Jay A. Levenson and Arthur M. Sackler Gallery, Washington D.C., 2007.

LIPINSKY, Angelo, "Il Tesoro di San Giovanni in Lisbona", in *Fede e Arte*, vol. IX, n.p., 1961, pp. 56-89.

LOBO ANTUNES, Mary Salgado, PINTO DE MATOS, Maria Antónia, *Porcelanas da China – Colecção Ricardo do Espírito Santo Silva*, Fundação Ricardo do Espírito Santo Silva, Museu-Escola de Artes Decorativas Portuguesas, Lisbon, 2000.

LOBO ANTUNES, Mary Salgado, *Porcelanas*, Fundação Ricardo do Espírito Santo Silva, Museu-Escola de Artes Decorativas Portuguesas, Lisbon, 1999.

MACHADO, José Alberto Gomes, *André Gonçalves Pintor do Barroco Português*, Estampa, Lisbon, 1995.

MADEIRA RODRIGUES, Maria João, *Museu de Arte Sacra de São Roque*, Santa Casa da Misericórdia de Lisboa/Museu de São Roque, Lisbon, 1964.

MADEIRA RODRIGUES, Maria João, *Pintura, Pratas, Tecidos*, Santa Casa da Misericórdia de Lisboa/Museu de São Roque, Lisbon, [1968].

MADEIRA RODRIGUES, Maria João, *O Mestre da Lenda de São Roque*, Santa Casa da Misericórdia de Lisboa/Museu de São Roque, Lisbon, 1973.

MADEIRA RODRIGUES, Maria João, *Arquitectura, Igreja e Casa Professa de S. Roque*, Colecção Cadernos de Conservação, Santa Casa da Misericórdia de Lisboa/Museu de São Roque, Lisbon, 1988.

MADEIRA RODRIGUES, Maria João, *A Capela de S. João Baptista e as suas Colecções*, Inapa, Lisbon, 1988.

MADEIRA RODRIGUES, Maria João, *La Chapelle de Saint Jean-Baptiste et ses collections en l'Église Saint Roch, à Lisbonne*, Inapa, Lisbon, 1988.

MADEIRA RODRIGUES, Maria João, *The Chapel of Saint John the Baptist and its collections*, Inapa, Lisbon, 1988.

MADEIRA RODRIGUES, Maria João, *Museu de São Roque. Metais*, 2nd edition, Santa Casa da Misericórdia de Lisboa/Museu de São Roque, Lisbon, 1988.

MANDROUX-FRANÇA, Marie-Thérèse, "La Patriarcale du Roi Jean V de Portugal", in *Colóquio-Artes*, 2.ª Série, no. 83, Lisbon, 1989, pp. 34-43.

MARQUES HENRIQUES, António Meira, "Iconografia de S. Francisco Xavier em S. Roque", in *Brotéria Cristianismo e Cultura – S. Francisco Xavier – no V centenário do seu Nascimento*, 5/6, vol. 163, Lisbon, 2006, pp. 417-430.

MARQUES HENRIQUES, António Meira, *São Francisco Xavier – Vida e Lenda*, colecção Ciclos Pictóricos, vol. I, Santa Casa da Misericórdia de Lisboa/Museu de São Roque, Lisbon, 2006.

Memoria do Descobrimento e Achado das Sagradas Relíquias do Antigo Santuário da Igreja de S. Roque, Imprensa Nacional, Lisbon, 1843.

MENDES PINTO, Maria Helena, *Lacas Namban em Portugal: presença portuguesa no Japão*, Inapa, Lisbon, 1990.

MENDONÇA, Maria José de, *Exposição dos Primitivos portugueses*, Museu Nacional de Arte Antiga, Lisbon, 1940.

MESSINGER, Sylvie, BIANCHINI, Marie-Claude, RAMOS, António, (coord.), *Do Tejo aos Mares da China. Uma epopeia portuguesa*, Palácio Nacional de Queluz – Instituto Português do Património Arquitectónico / Réunion des Musées Nationaux, Paris, 1992.

MOITINHO DE ALMEIDA, Fernando, *Marcas de Pratas Portuguesas e Brasileiras – Século XV a 1887*, Imprensa Nacional-Casa da Moeda, Lisbon, 1995.

MONTAGU, Jennifer, *Gold, Silver and Bronze. Metal Sculpture of the Roman Baroque*, Yale University Press, New Haven – London, 1996.

MONTERROSO TEIXEIRA, José, (coord.), *O Triunfo do Barroco*, Fundação das Descobertas, Centro Cultural de Belém, Lisbon, 1993.

MORNA, Teresa Freitas, (coord.), *A Ermida Manuelina de S. Roque*, Santa Casa da Misericórdia de Lisboa/Museu de São Roque, Lisbon, 1999.

MORNA, Teresa Freitas, (coord.), *Escultura – Século XVI ao Século XX, Colecção de Escultura da Misericórdia de Lisboa*, Colecção Património Artístico, Histórico e Cultural da Santa Casa da Misericórdia de Lisboa, vol. VI, Santa Casa da Misericórdia de Lisboa/Museu de São Roque, Lisbon, 2000.

MORNA, Teresa Freitas, (coord.), *Colecção Rodrigues Alves. Uma Herança da Misericórdia de Lisboa*, Colecção Património Artístico, Histórico e Cultural da Santa Casa da Misericórdia de Lisboa, vol. VIII, Santa Casa da Misericórdia de Lisboa/Museu de São Roque, Lisbon, 2003.

MORNA, Teresa Freitas, (coord.), *Os Jogos Sociais da Santa Casa da Misericórdia de Lisboa. Ao serviço de boas causas*, Santa Casa da Misericórdia de Lisboa/Museu de São Roque, Lisbon, 2004.

MORNA, Teresa Freitas, (coord.), *100 Anos Museu de São Roque. 1905-2005*, Santa Casa da Misericórdia de Lisboa/Museu de São Roque, Lisbon, 2005.

MORNA, Teresa Freitas, (coord.), *Museum of São Roque*, (exhibition catalogue), Santa Casa da Misericórdia de Lisboa/Museu de São Roque, Lisbon, 2008.

MOURA, Carlos, *História da Arte em Portugal. O Limiar do Barroco*, vol. VIII, Alfa, Lisbon, 1986.

MOURA CARVALHO, Pedro de, (coord.), *O Mundo da Laca – 2000 anos de História*, Museu Calouste Gulbenkian, Lisbon, 2001.

MOURA SOBRAL, Luís de, *Pintura e Poesia na Época Barroca*, Estampa, Lisbon, 1994.

MOURA SOBRAL, Luís de, (coord.), *Bento Coelho da Silveira (1620-1708) e a Cultura do Seu Tempo*, Galeria de Pintura do Rei D. Luís, Instituto Português do Património Arquitectónico, Lisbon, 1996.

MOURA SOBRAL, Luís de, *Do Sentido das Imagens*, Estampa, Lisbon, 1996.

MOURA SOBRAL, Luís de, *Pintura Portuguesa do Século XVII, Histórias, Lendas, Narrativas*, MNAA, Lisbon, 2004.

Novos Mundos/Neue Welten: os Descobrimentos Portugueses (séculos XV a XVII), Deutsches Historisches Museum, Berlin, 2007/2008.

Object i memòria, Museu Frederic Marès, Barcelona, 2004.

PAMPLONA, Fernando de, *Dicionário de Pintores e Escultores Portugueses*, 5 vols, 4th edition, Livraria Civilização Editora, Lisbon, 2000.

PAULINO, Francisco Faria, (coord.), *A Expansão Portuguesa e a Arte de Marfim*, Comissão Nacional para as Comemorações dos Descobrimentos Portugueses, Fundação Calouste Gulbenkian, Lisbon, 1991.

PAULINO, Francisco Faria, (coord.), *A Pintura Maneirista em Portugal. A Arte no Tempo de Camões*, Comissão Nacional para as Comemorações dos Descobrimentos Portugueses, Lisbon, 1995.

PEREIRA, José Fernandes, PEREIRA, Paulo, (coord.), *Dicionário da Arte Barroca em Portugal*, Editoral Presença, Lisbon, 1989.

PIMENTEL, António Filipe, *Arquitectura e poder: o real edifício de Mafra*, colection Subsídios para a História da Arte Portuguesa, Instituto de História da Arte da Faculdade de Letras da Universidade de Coimbra, Coimbra, 1992.

PIMENTEL, António Filipe, "Uma jóia em forma de templo: a Capela de São João Baptista", in *Oceanos*, no. 43, Lisbon, July/September, 2000, pp. 146-164.

PIMENTEL, António Filipe, "Nobre, séria e rica: a encomenda da capela lisboeta de S. João Baptista em S. Roque e a controvérsia Barroco *versus* Classicismo", in PEREIRA, Sónia Gomes (org.), *Anais do VI Colóquio Luso-Brasileiro de História da Arte*, vol. I, Rio de Janeiro, n.no., 2004, pp. 99-134.

PINTO DE MATOS, Maria Antónia, (coord.), *Portugal e Flandres. Visões da Europa 1550-1680*, Instituto Português do Património Cultural, Lisbon, 1992.

QUIETO, Pier Paolo, *D. João V de Portugal e a Sua Influência na Arte Italiana do Século XVIII*, Elo, Lisbon – Mafra, 1990.

RACZYNSKI, *Les Arts en Portugal*, Jules Renouard, Paris, 1846.

RACZYNSKI, *Diccionnaire Histórico-artistique*, Jules Renouard, Paris, 1847.

RAMOS, José da Silva, "Museu de Arte Sacra", in *Guia de Portugal Artístico*, vol. IV, M. Costa Ramalho, Lisbon, 1934, pp. 25-60.

RÉAU, Louis, *Iconografia del arte Cristiano*, Vol. I a VI, Ed. Serbal, Barcelona, 1996.

RIBEIRO, Victor, *A Santa Casa da Misericórdia de Lisboa. Subsídios para a sua História*, Academia das Ciências, Lisbon, 1998, (fac-simile of the 1902 edition).

ROCCA, Sandra Vasco, (coord.), *Dizionari Terminologici Suppellettile Ecclesiastica*, vol. I, Ministero per i Beni Culturali e Ambientali/Istituto Centrale per il Catalogo i la Documentazione, Florence, 1988.

ROCCA, Sandra Vasco, BORGHINI, Gabriele, (coord.), *Giovanni V di Portogallo e la Cultura Romana del suo Tempo*, Àrgos Edizioni, Rome, 1995.

RODRIGUES, Dalila, (coord.), *Grão Vasco e a Pintura Europeia do Renascimento*, Comissão Nacional para as Comemorações dos Descobrimentos Portugueses, Lisbon, 1992.

ROISIN, Brigitte, VERSTRAETE, John, GODEAUX, Hélène, (coord.), *Le Triomphe du Baroque*, Palais de Beaux-Arts de Bruxelles, Fondation Europalia International, Brussels, 1991.

SALDANHA, Nuno, *Artistas, Imagens, e Ideias na Pintura do Século XVIII*, vol. I, Livros Horizonte, Lisbon, 1995.

SANTOS CARVALHO, José dos, *São Roque e os Seus Artistas*, Separata da "Revista Municipal", n.º 58, Câmara Municipal de Lisboa, Lisbon, 1953.

São *Francisco Xavier – A Sua Vida e o Seu Tempo*, Comissariado Geral das Comemorações do V Centenário do Nascimento de S. Francisco Xavier, Lisbon, 2006.

SERRÃO, Joel (coord.), *Dicionário de História de Portugal*, vols. 1 a 6, Livraria Figueirinhas, Oporto, 1992.

SERRÃO, Vítor, *A pintura maneirista em Portugal*, Colecção Biblioteca Breve. Série Artes Visuais, n.º 65, Instituto de Cultura e Língua Portuguesa. Ministério da Educação e das Universidades, Lisbon, 1982.

SERRÃO, Vítor, *História da Arte em Portugal – O Maneirismo*, vol. 7, Alfa, Lisbon, 1986.

SERRÃO, Vítor, *Estudos de Pintura Maneirista e Barroca*, Caminho, Lisbon, 1989.

SERRÃO, Vítor, *A Pintura Proto-Barroca em Portugal, 1612-1657*, vols. I and II, Doctoral Dissertation presented in Faculdade de Letras – Universidade de Coimbra, (type-written text), Coimbra, 1992.

SOARES DA CUNHA, Mafalda, (coord.), *Os Construtores do Oriente Português*, Comissão Nacional para as Comemorações dos Descobrimentos Portugueses, Oporto, 1998.

SOUSA FRANCO, Matilde, *Museu de S. Roque*, Santa Casa de Misericórdia de Lisboa/Museu de São Roque, Lisbon, 1992.

TAVARES E TÁVORA, Bernardo Ferrão de, *Imaginária luso-oriental*, Imprensa Nacional – Casa da Moeda, Lisbon, 1983.

TAVARES, *Dicionário de Santos*, Lello e Irmão Editores, Oporto, 1990.

TCHAKALOFF, Thierry-Nicolas, (coord.), *La Route des Indes*, Musée d'Aquitaine, Bordeaux, 1998.

TELFER, M.A.W., *The Treasure of São Roque – A sidelight on the Counter-Reformation*, Society for Promoting Christian Knowledge, London, 1932.

TELLES, Baltazar, *Chronica da Companhia de Jesus na Provincia de Portugal*, vol. II, Paulo Craesbeeck, Lisbon, 1645.

The Age of the Baroque in Portugal, National Gallery of Art, Washington D.C., Ed. Jay A. Levenson, Washington D.C., 1993.

The Triumph of Baroque. Architecture in Europe 1600-1750, Palazzo Grassi, Ed. Bompiani, Venice, 1999.

TRNEK, Helmut, VASSALLO E SILVA, Nuno, (coord.), *Exótica – Os Descobrimentos Portugueses e as Câmaras de Maravilhas do Renascimento*, Fundação Calouste Gulbenkian, Lisbon, 2001.

VALE, Teresa Leonor M., *Da Igreja Combatente à Igreja Triunfante. Espaço e Imagem Religiosa do Concílio de Trento ao Barroco Pleno*, separata de "Brotéria", vol. 157, Lisbon, 2003.

VALE, Teresa Leonor M. (coord. de), *Lisboa Barroca e o Barroco de Lisboa*, Livros Horizonte, Lisbon, 2007.

VASSALLO E SILVA, Nuno, (coord.), *No Caminho do Japão – Arte Oriental nas Colecções da Santa Casa da Misericórdia de Lisboa*, Santa Casa da Misericórdia de Lisboa/Museu de São Roque, Lisbon, 1993.

VASSALLO E SILVA, Nuno, (coord.), *Azulejos – Painéis do Século XVI ao Século XX*, Colecção Património Artístico, Histórico e Cultural da Santa Casa da Misericórdia de Lisboa, vol. I, Santa Casa da Misericórdia de Lisboa/Museu de São Roque, Lisbon, 1994.

VASSALLO E SILVA, Nuno, (coord.), *Frontais de Altar Seiscentistas da Igreja de São Roque*, Santa Casa da Misericórdia de Lisboa/Museu de São Roque, Lisbon, 1994.

VASSALLO E SILVA, Nuno, (coord.), *Natividade em S. Roque*, Santa Casa da Misericórdia de Lisboa/Museu de São Roque, Lisbon, 1994.

VASSALLO E SILVA, Nuno, (coord.), *A Herança de Rauluchantim*, Santa Casa da Misericórdia de Lisboa/Museu de São Roque/Comissão Nacional para as Comemorações dos Descobrimentos Portugueses, Lisbon, 1996.

VASSALLO E SILVA, Nuno, (coord.), *O Púlpito e a Imagem – os Jesuítas e a Arte*, Santa Casa da Misericórdia de Lisboa/Museu de São Roque, Lisbon, 1996.

VASSALLO E SILVA, Nuno, (coord.), *Símbolos e Imagens – Reflexos do Cristianismo na Porcelana Chinesa*, Santa Casa da Misericórdia de Lisboa/Museu de São Roque, Lisbon, 1996.

VASSALLO E SILVA, Nuno, (coord.), *Convento de S. Pedro de Alcântara*, Santa Casa da Misericórdia de Lisboa/Museu de São Roque, Lisbon, 1997.

VASSALLO E SILVA, Nuno, (coord.), *Esplendor e Devoção*, Colecção Património Artístico, Histórico e Cultural da Santa Casa da Misericórdia de Lisboa, vol. III, Santa Casa da Misericórdia de Lisboa/Museu de São Roque, Lisbon, 1998.

VASSALLO E SILVA, Nuno, (coord.), *Mater Misericordiae*, Santa Casa da Misericórdia/Museu de São Roque/Livros Horizonte, Lisbon, 1998.

VASSALLO E SILVA, Nuno, (coord.), *Ourivesaria e Iluminura. Século XIV ao Século XX*, Colecção Património Artístico, Histórico e Cultural da Santa Casa da Misericórdia de Lisboa, vol. IV, Santa Casa da Misericórdia de Lisboa/Museu de São Roque, Lisbon, 1998.

PINTO DE MATOS, Maria Antónia, (coord.), *Via Orientalis*, Európália, Brussels, 1991.

VITERBO, Francisco Marques de Sousa, ALMEIDA, Rodrigo Vicente d', *A Capella de S. João Baptista Erecta na Egreja de S. Roque. Fundação da Companhia de Jesus e Hoje Pertencente à Santa Casa da Misericordia. Noticia Historica e Descriptiva*, Livros Horizonte, Lisbon, 1997, (fac-simile of the 1902 edition).

VOLKMAR MACHADO, Cyrillo, *Collecção de memórias relativas ás vidas dos pintores e escultores, architectos, e estrangeiros, que estiverão em Portugal*, Imprensa da Universidade, Coimbra, 1922.